Common
MUSHROOMS
of the Northwest

Alaska, Western Canada
& the Northwestern United States

Clustered Collybia *Gymnopus acervatus*

J. Duane Sept

Calypso Publishing

All photographs by J. Duane Sept except for the photographs of man on horseback (p. 27), meadow mushroom (p. 39), the prince (p. 40), and liberty cap (p. 45). by Michael Beug. The photograph of the author by Susan Servos-Sept (p. 95).
Front cover photos: Pleated marasmius, western amethyst laccaria, glistening inkcap, shaggy mane and smoky-gilled woodlover by J. Duane Sept.
Back cover photos: Panther amanita and common laccaria by J. Duane Sept.
Printed and bound in India.

Calypso Publishing　　　　　　　　　www.calypso-publishing.com
P. O. Box 1141
Sechelt, BC Canada
V0N 3A0

Duane Sept Photography　　　　　　　　www.septphoto.com

Library and Archives Canada Cataloguing in Publication

Sept, J. Duane, 1950-
　　　　Common mushrooms of the Northwest : Alaska, western Canada and the northwestern United States / J. Duane Sept, author and photographer. --
1st ed.

Includes bibliographical references and index.
ISBN 0-9739819-0-3

　　　　1. Mushrooms--Northwest, Pacific--Identification. 2. Mushrooms--Canada, Western--Identification. 3. Mushrooms--Alaska--Identification. I. Title.

QK617.S385 2006　　　　　　　579.6'09795　　　　　　C2006-900770-5

CAUTION!
The purpose of this guide is not to identify edible mushrooms but rather to encourage readers to appreciate the variety and significance of fungi. **Many species of mushrooms are poisonous—and some are deadly.** Other mushrooms, including edible species, may cause allergic reactions or unexplained physical responses. All information contained in this book is accurate to the best of the author's knowledge. The author, publisher, distributor and bookseller assume no liability for the actions of the reader. Many of the mushrooms listed here are **toxic** and **must not be ingested.** If you wish to eat wild mushrooms, verify your identifications with a mushroom expert. Beginners should never eat any wild mushroom until a mushroom expert confirms the species. **Be cautious.**

Contents

Introduction

Mushrooms are not animals or plants; instead they belong to a kingdom that they share with other fungi, including molds and yeasts.
Fungi were once believed to be part of the plant kingdom, but scientists now know that they have little in common with plants. Mycologists—scientists that study mushrooms—believe that there may be as
many as 10,000 species of fungi living in the Pacific Northwest and
up to 1.5 million species worldwide. Many of them have not yet been
identified.

What Is a Mushroom?

Mushrooms are the reproductive structures or fruiting bodies of fungi
that live in a particular medium—in the ground, in wood or even in
the body of an insect or other organism. The main body of a fungus
consists of many mycelia, the eating part of the fungus. Each mycelium (singular of "mycelia") is made up of several hyphae (pronounced
HIGH-fee), which lie side by side and work together as a group.
Hyphae make up various parts of the fruiting body as well.

For a mushroom to reproduce, it must produce seed-like structures
called spores. Thousands or even millions of these spores are produced
in each fruiting body, then released into the environment. Some of
the spores settle in suitable places to grow, and the life cycle begins
again.

Mushrooms and Their Environment

Wherever they live, mushrooms and all fungi are an important part of
their ecosystems. They are associated with other organisms in three
ways.

Symbiotic Mushrooms
In symbiotic situations, the mushroom's mycelia form a special association with the roots of a tree or other plant, and both organisms
benefit. The plant's growth is accelerated as a result of fungi deliver-
ing nitrogen and phosphorus, and the mushroom obtains carbohy-
drates in return.

Parasitic Mushrooms
Mushroom parasites feed on or live off another living organism. In this situation, only one organism—the mushroom—benefits, and the health of the host is often in jeopardy. The honey mushroom, *Armillaria mellea* complex, is one of the best-known parasitic fungi.

Saprophytic Mushrooms
The fungal species in this large group feed on a variety of dead organic matter, including rotting wood and soil. The oyster mushroom, *Pleurotus ostreatus*, is a well-known saprophytic mushroom.

Identifying Mushrooms

Since there is such a large number of mushroom species growing in the Northwest, most species are not readily identifiable. This guidebook focuses on species that can be identified easily by appearance, rather than by examination with a microscope. Many of the others are often affectionately lumped into the classifications BUMs (boring ubiquitous mushrooms), LBMs (little brown mushrooms) or SLMs (standard lawn mushrooms). They cannot be positively identified without further detailed study. Start by learning to identify the common, identifiable species—the more difficult ones will come easier later on. To learn more about the mushrooms in your area, consider joining a local mushroom club or association (see p. 9).

Several websites are also very helpful, offering a wide selection of images and information on some species. Helpful websites that were up and running early in 2006 include:

BC Mushrooms
http://bcmushrooms.forrex.org/

CalPhotos: Fungi
http://calphotos.berkeley.edu/fungi/

The Fungi of California
http://www.mykoweb.com/CAF/species_index.html

Fungi Images on the Net
http://fungi.fvlmedia.dk/

Fungi of Saskatchewan
http://www.usask.ca/biology/fungi/home_%20page.shtml

Matchmaker: Mushrooms of the Pacific Northwest
http://www.pfc.forestry.ca/cgi-bin/matchmaker/matchmaker.asp

MushroomExpert.com
http://www.mushroomexpert.com/

Pacific Northwest Key Council
http://www.svims.ca/council/council.htm

Pamela's Mushrooms
http://www.pamelasmushrooms.com/

Taylor Lockwood's FungiPhoto
http://www.fungiphoto.com/

Edible Mushrooms

For edibility, mushrooms can be rated from choice to deadly poisonous. In this book, edibility has been included as a category in the
basic information for each species. Please note, however, that this
book is not a guide to finding edible mushrooms. If you plan to eat
any fungi, be sure you are very familiar with that species from past
experience, or talk to a mushroom expert. Then taste only a small
portion to ensure that it does not cause you any discomfort, and wait
a minimum of 48 hours before eating any more of that species or any
other. Poisonings occur occasionally with edible species, and it is not
known how, why or when this happens. Some edible mushrooms are
poisonous unless thoroughly cooked. Remember to cook all mushrooms
before eating, unless the guide states specifically that a species is
edible raw.

It should also be noted that there are no shortcuts in identifying edible and poisonous species of mushrooms. Many fungi are similar, and
the edible and poisonous species must be studied together in order to
be distinguished. Get the help of a mushroom expert with any species
that are unfamiliar or that you are uncertain about.

If you observe wildlife feeding on mushrooms, do not assume that those species are edible by humans. The metabolism of a squirrel, for instance, is much different than that of a human! Harvest only the ones you are absolutely sure about, or that have been identified positively by an expert. Fungi are the preferred food of a wide range of creatures, including maggots. So be sure to check your pickings in the field—before you bring back live stowaways!

Allergic Reactions

Allergic reactions may occur with mushrooms, as with any food or other substance. A rash, swollen lips or other symptoms may occur. Consume only moderate amounts of any mushroom you know to be edible. Try only a small portion of a species that is new to you. **Caution is advised!**

Mushroom Poisoning

Mushroom poisoning can affect several organs of the body, producing a range of effects including death. As little as 1.7 ounces (50 grams), or one small specimen of death cap *Amanita phalloides*, can kill an adult. In addition, it takes six to 24 hours for the symptoms of ama-toxin (a very dangerous group of poisons with a 50% mortality rate) to begin to show, by which time it is too late—unless you have a liver or kidney transplant. **Caution is advised!**

If you suspect any kind of mushroom poisoning, don't wait for symptoms to appear. Contact a physician immediately, and provide a specimen of the mushroom in question if possible.

Several poison centers across North America are equipped to deal with mushroom poisoning. In some areas, general information on poisoning can be obtained by dialing 911 on the telephone. For a poisoning emergency or suspected poisoning in the Northwest, contact the appropriate number below:

Alberta Poison Center 1-800-332-1414
BC Drug & Poison Emergency Center 1-800-567-8911
Saskatchewan Poison Center 1-866-454-1212
United States Poison Control Center 1-800-222-1222

Hallucinogenic Mushrooms

Some species of mushrooms have hallucinogenic properties. In some cases the hallucinogenic effect is caused by the first stage of mushroom poisoning. Other species (e.g. *Psilocybe* sp.) are well known for their mind-altering effects. Once again, **caution is advised**.

How to Use This Guide

This guide, designed to give information on and help identify common mushrooms and other fungi found throughout the Northwest, includes two types of fungi: basidiomycetes (true mushrooms) and ascomycetes (sac fungi).

FAMILY
A mushroom family is a grouping of one or more genera with similar overall characteristics. All Boletes, for instance, belong to the family Boletaceae, which includes many genera.

SPECIES
A common and a scientific name are listed for each species. Every living organism has a unique scientific name consisting of two parts: the genus (a grouping of species with common characteristics) and the species. Occasionally names change as new scientific information is discovered. The most current or appropriate name is included in this book.

Common names are those used in everyday conversation by people who live in an area where the species occur, so many plants have several common names. The most widely accepted common name appears at the top of each entry with the species' scientific name.

ADDITIONAL NAMES
Other common names and scientific names for the species are listed here.

DESCRIPTION
To identify a species, use the photograph and the written description together. Data on the cap, stem and size accompany a description of the mushroom or fungus. Together these features will help you identify many common species. Cap and stem colors can vary significantly within a region, so use the notes on color as a general guide in the field. The maximum size of each species is also given.

SEASON
Each entry lists the month in which the fruiting body is visible.

HABITAT
Habitat is the type of surroundings in which a species normally grows. Many common mushrooms and fungi are found in more than one habitat; some have specific moisture requirements.

RANGE
Range is the physical location where the species is known to grow.

EDIBILITY
Some mushroom species can be safely eaten by humans, and for edibility, mushrooms can range from choice to poisonous. Edible species can have similar-looking poisonous species growing nearby or immediately adjacent. Examine each specimen carefully. Discard any specimens that do not appear to be the desired species. Before eating or tasting anything, contact a mushroom expert to confirm the identification of any species that you are not sure about. The information included here is the general consensus. Experts' opinions vary. Moderation in eating any wild species is advised. Allergic reactions can also be triggered by any type of food. Do not eat anything that you cannot identify confidently as edible. Many of the species included in this book are toxic and must not be ingested. Look for the warning **toxic** or **poisonous** in the edibility section.

NOTES
Notes accompanying each species give special information, such as interesting features of the fungi and other facts of interest.

SIMILAR SPECIES
Species that are similar in appearance are identified, along with notes and additional information.

Mycological Associations of the Northwest

One of the best ways to observe, learn about and identify mushrooms is to join a local mushroom or mycological organization. These groups meet regularly and bring in guest speakers on various topics related to mushrooms. Field trips or forays are a main focus for these clubs. Here, new members join the more experienced individuals to search for and learn about mushrooms. Look for the most current contact information for these groups on the Internet. The following websites, which were current early in 2006, are a good introduction to mycological associations and clubs throughout the Northwest and beyond.

The North American Mycological Association (NAMA)
http://www.namyco.org/

The North American Mycological Societies
http://www.mykoweb.com/na_mycos.html

A Canadian Mycological Resource
http://www.fungi.ca/mycogroups.htm

Spore Prints

In many instances the identification of fungi relies on the color of the spores that each species produces. In order to determine the spore color, a spore print can easily be made. Separate the cap of the mushroom from its stem. Place the cap on a piece of paper. For the best visibility, use colored paper if the spores are white, and white paper if they are colored. Leave the cap on the paper overnight, covered with a bowl or similar protective object to prevent air currents from dispersing the spores. Carefully remove the bowl the following morning to reveal the color of the spore print. Some people also create artwork with spore prints.

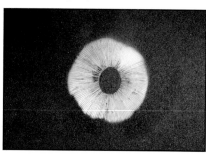

White spore print.

Key to the Spore Print Colors

 Light-spored Fungi

 Dark-spored Fungi

 Brown-spored Fungi

 Pink-spored Fungi

The Parts of a Mushroom

cap

warts (remnants of veil)

gills

ring (annulus)

stalk (stipe)

volva

Fly Amanita *Amanita muscaria*

cap

volva

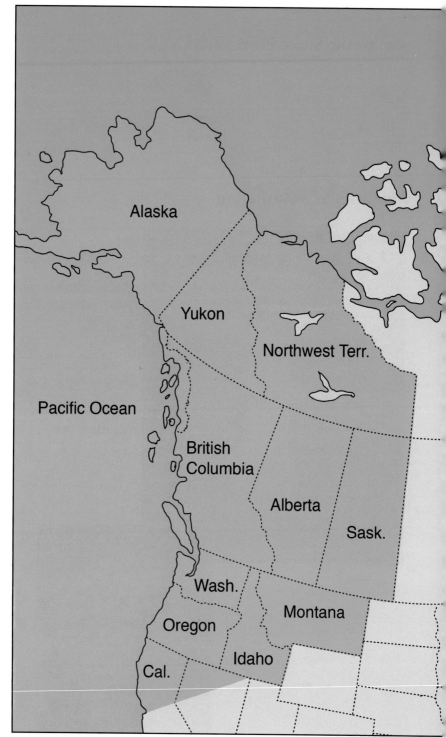

Figure 1. Geographic area covered in this guide.

BASIDIOMYCETES

Basidiomycetes are the division of the fungi kingdom that produce their spores on basidia (microscopic, club-like structures), which are attached to the exterior of the fruiting body.

Bleeding Mycena *Mycena haematopus*.

Delicious Milk Cap *Lactarius deliciosus*

Other Names Delicious lactarius, orange delicious, saffron milk cap, orange latex milky.
Description Scattered or in small groups. **Spore Print:** Cream. **Cap:** Orange-brown; broadly convex with a depressed center; margin inrolled, becoming vase-shaped as it ages; surface smooth, slimy when moist; stains green when bruised; flesh brittle. **Gills:** Orange to yellowish orange; crowded; may produce orange milk, stains green when bruised. **Stalk:** Orange-brown; often narrower at base. **Size:** Cap to 6⅓" (16 cm) across. Stalk to 2¾" (7 cm) long.
Season August to October.
Habitat On the ground under conifers, especially pine.
Range Widely distributed in North America.
Edibility Edible and good, but not always as delicious as the name would lead you to expect.

Notes This is a distinctive species with its combination of orange color, orange milk and green-staining flesh. How can you go wrong with a mushroom that has "*deliciosis*" in its scientific name? In some countries, this species is used in a wide variety of dishes, in appreciation for its spicy herb-like flavor. This species is said to be great when marinated. Please note that eating these fungi often turns the urine red—a normal reaction and not an indication of a poison.

Similar Species Bleeding Milk Cap *Lactarius rubrilacteus*, also a common species, especially in young Douglas-fir forests. It stains green as well, but oozes dark red milk from its reddish gills. Happily, it is quite edible.

Red Hot Milk Cap *Lactarius rufus*

Other Name Red-hot milky.
Description Scattered or in small groups. **Spore Print:** Off-white to yellowish. **Cap:** Red; convex to flat or slightly depressed; surface smooth and dry; produces a white, milk-like latex. **Gills:** Off-white maturing to reddish; crowded; adnate (attached). **Stalk:** Red; fragile.

Size: Cap to 4¾" (12 cm) across. Stalk to 4⅓" (11 cm) long.
Season August to November.
Habitat On the ground under conifers, especially pines in bogs and also deciduous trees.
Range Pacific Northwest, northern California.
Edibility Listed as poisonous by some authorities; but this species and others are harvested and canned in Scandinavia, where they are sold. The North American variants have yet to be tested—this species could be poisonous. **Do not eat it.**
Notes If you taste this species carefully, without actually eating it, you will find that it is mild tasting at first, then it has a strong peppery taste that takes longer to be noticed. The red hot milk cap is a common species, especially under pines in bogs, and is easily recognized by its overall bright red color and white latex that does not change color.

Short-stemmed Russula *Russula brevipes*

Other Names Short-stalked white russula, stubby brittlegill.
Description Solitary to scattered or in small groups.
Spore Print: White to pale buff. **Cap:** Off-white, often brown-stained but normally covered in dirt; top convex, maturing to funnel-shaped; margin inrolled; surface dry and dull; flesh very firm and thick. **Gills:** White, may be tinged with blue; crowded and narrow. **Stalk:** White, often brown-stained; short and stocky; tough and rigid. **Size:** Cap to 12" (30 cm) across. Stalk to 4" (10 cm) long.
Season July to December.
Habitat On the ground in coniferous and deciduous forests.
Range Widely distributed in North America.
Edibility Generally considered not worth eating; however, one reference states that it may be eaten if it is cooked for a long time in soups and stews. Be sure to remove any dirt and needles that cling to the outside of this species before cooking.
Notes The short-stemmed russula is a large, unattractive, abundant species that is generally ignored by pickers. It was long thought to be the same as *Russula delica*, a similar-looking fungus from Europe, but scientists now believe that the European species does not occur in North America.

 # Cascade Russula *Russula cascadensis*

Description Solitary to scattered or in small groups. **Spore Print:** White. **Cap:** Off-white, often with a yellowish tinge; top convex maturing to funnel-shaped; surface dry, smooth and waxy; flesh very firm and thick. **Gills:** White; coarse and well-spaced. **Stalk:** Off-white; firm. **Size:** Cap to 9" (22 cm) across. Stalk to 2" (5 cm) long.
Season August to November.
Habitat On the ground in coniferous and mixed-woods forests.
Range Pacific Northwest to northern California and the Rocky Mountains.
Edibility Edible with a peppery taste that disappears upon cooking.
Notes This species develops underground, much like the short-stemmed russula, pushing its way to the surface with dirt adhering to its cap. The Cascade russula forms mycorrhizal (symbiotic) relationships with the conifers under which it grows.
Similar Species Short-stemmed Russula *Russula brevipes,* a larger species that does not have a peppery taste (see above).

Blackening Russula *Russula nigricans*

Description Solitary to small groups. **Spore Print:** White. **Cap:** White turning to brown and eventually black; top convex changing to depressed; surface dry to sticky; flesh bruises red then turns black; hard. **Gills:** Cream to gray then black; widely spaced; alternating short and long; brittle. **Stalk:** White or cream changing to black; short and stout; solid. **Size:** Cap to 10" (25 cm) across. Stalk to 3¼" (8 cm).
Season July to September.
Habitat On the ground in coniferous and deciduous forests.
Range Northern region of North America; Pacific Northwest and the Rocky Mountains.
Edibility Rated in some references as edible when young, before turning black. Similar species are poisonous. **Do not eat.**
Notes The blackening russula is a distinctive species that is solid and dry with distant gills and flesh that stains red prior to turning black. It is a common species, often noticed after it reaches a large size and turns totally black.

 # Rosy Russula *Russula sanguinea*

Other Names Rose-red russula; also known as *Russula rosacea*.
Description Scattered or in groups. **Spore Print:** White to creamy. **Cap:** Red fading to pink; top convex to slightly depressed; surface smooth, viscid (sticky) when wet; flesh firm and brittle. **Gills:** Creamy white to light yellow; crowded, forked near stem. **Stalk:** White tinted with pink; hollow when aged. **Size:** Cap to 4¾" (12 cm) across. Stalk to 4" (10 cm) long.
Season July to October.
Habitat On the ground under coniferous trees, especially pine.
Range Widely distributed in North America.
Edibility Not edible.

Notes The flesh of the rosy russula is very brittle, as in all members of this family. This species has a strong peppery taste. This, along with its rosy stem, aid in identifying it. If you taste this species for identification, do not swallow its flesh—just as in any mushroom taste testing.

Fragile Russula *Russula fragilis*

Description Solitary or in small groups.
Spore Print: White. **Cap:** Varies widely: pink or purplish to olive-brown, green or yellow, normally with several of these colors present on the same specimen; convex to depressed; surface smooth and sticky when wet; flesh very fragile. **Gills:** White to cream; crowded.
Stalk: White; fragile. **Size:** Cap to 2" (5 cm) across. Stalk to 2¾" (7 cm) long.
Season July to September.
Habitat On the ground or on rotting wood, in mixed-woods and coniferous forests.
Range Widely distributed in North America.
Edibility Not edible.

Notes Reddish pink is the most common color of the fragile russula, but it fades and becomes whitish as it ages. The russulas are well known for being a somewhat difficult group to identify to individual species. The fragile russula is one of several look-alikes in the Northwest that have a variable cap color. Detailed information—such as habitat, spore color, texture and taste—is required for correct identification within this species complex. It is often difficult even for experts to identify these species correctly.

Similar Species **Emetic Russula** *Russula emetica*, very similar in appearance with a bright red cap and a preference for growing near coniferous trees in sphagnum bogs. In the past, many russulas were often misidentified as this species. Its distribution in North America is currently under review.
Bicolored Russula *Russula bicolor*, displays a multicolored cap that stains pink or orange when bruised. It is often found growing under birch trees.

Miniature Waxy Cap *Hygrocybe miniata*

Other Names Vermilion waxcap, fading scarlet waxy cap; *Hygrophorus miniatus*.
Description Solitary to small groups. **Spore Print:** White. **Cap:** Bright red or orange fading to yellow; convex to flat or slightly depressed; surface smooth; flesh thin, waxy. **Gills:** Red fading to yellow; soft and waxy. **Stalk:** Red fading to yellow. **Veil:** Absent. **Size:** Cap to 1½" (4 cm) across. Stalk to 3¼" (8 cm) long.
Season July to November; October to February in California.
Habitat On the ground, in the shade of mixed-woods and coniferous forests, as well as on rotting wood.
Range Widely distributed in North America.
Edibility Edible but bland.
Notes Miniature waxy cap is a brilliant touch of color added to the forest floor. Its vivid hues are remarkable in such a small species but they fade in time to become much more subdued. A few closely related species may be found, but they are not easily distinguished from this one without a microscope. This is the most common species in the group.

 # Witch's Hat *Hygrocybe conica*

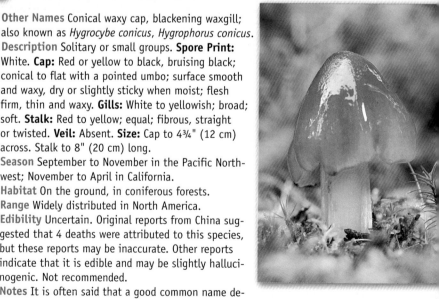

Other Names Conical waxy cap, blackening waxgill; also known as *Hygrocybe conicus*, *Hygrophorus conicus*.
Description Solitary or small groups. **Spore Print:** White. **Cap:** Red or yellow to black, bruising black; conical to flat with a pointed umbo; surface smooth and waxy, dry or slightly sticky when moist; flesh firm, thin and waxy. **Gills:** White to yellowish; broad; soft. **Stalk:** Red to yellow; equal; fibrous, straight or twisted. **Veil:** Absent. **Size:** Cap to 4¾" (12 cm) across. Stalk to 8" (20 cm) long.
Season September to November in the Pacific Northwest; November to April in California.
Habitat On the ground, in coniferous forests.
Range Widely distributed in North America.
Edibility Uncertain. Original reports from China suggested that 4 deaths were attributed to this species, but these reports may be inaccurate. Other reports indicate that it is edible and may be slightly hallucinogenic. Not recommended.
Notes It is often said that a good common name describes a species well, and this is certainly the case with witch's hat. This species is an easy mushroom to identify, with its distinctive "witch's hat" shape and its tendency to turn black after being handled or picked, or as it ages. If only all mushrooms were as easy to identify!

Oyster Mushroom *Pleurotus ostreatus*

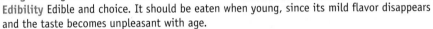

Description Solitary to clustered. **Spore Print:** White to lilac. **Cap:** White to dark brown; fan-shaped, top convex to flat or slightly depressed; surface smooth. **Gills:** White or gray, discoloring to yellowish on aging; crowded and narrow; decurrent (running down the stem) if stalk is present. **Stalk:** Normally absent, but a short lateral stalk may be present. **Size:** Cap to 6" (15 cm) across. Stalk to 1½" (4 cm) long when present. **Season** Spring and fall.
Habitat On deciduous wood, especially red alder, as well as on living deciduous trees and rarely on conifers.
Range Throughout North America.
Edibility Edible and choice. It should be eaten when young, since its mild flavor disappears and the taste becomes unpleasant with age.
Notes The shelf-like growth of the oyster mushroom, along with its smooth cap and white gills, are characteristic and very helpful in identifying this excellent-tasting mushroom. There are several variations within the oyster mushroom complex, and a few closely related species are members of it. Some species display a brown cap while others are white, and some have thin flesh while others have thick flesh. Luckily all types or species are edible and choice! Oyster mushrooms are now grown commercially and marketed as "tree oysters."

 # Angel Wings *Pleurotus porrigens*

Other Names *Pleurocybella porrigens, Pleurotellus porrigens.*
Description Small groups to clusters. **Spore Print:** White. **Cap:** White to cream-colored; fan-shaped or tongue-shaped; margin incurved when small; surface smooth; flesh thin. **Gills:** White to yellowish; crowded and narrow; decurrent if stalk is present. **Stalk:** Normally absent, but a short lateral stalk may be present. **Size:** To 4" (10 cm) long and 2" (5 cm) across.
Season September to October.

Habitat On coniferous stumps, trunks and logs.
Range Pacific Northwest and northern California.
Edibility Edible, with caution. In 2004, a total of 13 people died from consuming this species in Japan. All victims had kidney disorders and were on dialysis.
Notes The graceful look of this species is always a welcome sight while walking through the woods. It is easily identified by its characteristic thin, wavy top. This species is easily dried or even eaten raw, adding a nice touch to a green salad.

Late Oyster Mushroom *Panellus serotinus*

Other Names Late fall oyster, green oyster, winter panellus; formerly *Pleurotus serotinus*.
Description Scattered or in small groups.
Spore Print: Yellowish. **Cap:** Olive green, with or without violet tones; fan-shaped or kidney-shaped; margin incurved; surface with fine, short hairs, sticky when moist. **Gills:** Pale orange to pale yellow. **Stalk:** Normally absent, but a yellowish false stem base is present with dark flecks. **Size:** Cap to 6" (15 cm) across. Stalk to 1" (2.5 cm) long when present.
Season August to November.
Habitat On deciduous stumps and logs, especially alder.
Range Throughout much of North America.
Edibility Edible, but it often gets a mediocre rating.
Notes As its common name suggests, the late oyster mushroom fruits in the fall when the temperature dips near freezing. This edible species should be cooked slowly over a long time for the best results.
Similar Species **Pink Oyster** *Panellus longinquus*, a pale orange or pinkish species commonly found on alders in December and January.

 # False Oyster *Panellus mitis*

Other Names Elastic oysterling, kidney-shaped pleurotus; also known as *Panellus mitis*.
Description Solitary or in small groups. **Spore Print:** White. **Cap:** Creamy white; flat to broadly convex; gill edges are gelatinous and shell-shaped; surface covered in minute, dense white hair. **Gills:** White; narrow. **Stalk:** Normally absent, but a short lateral stalk may be present. **Size:** Cap to 5/16" (8 mm) across. Stalk to 1/16" (2 mm) long.
Season October to December.
Habitat On dead coniferous trees.
Range Pacific Northwest and the Rocky Mountains.
Edibility Unknown.

Notes Little is known about the false oyster. Molecular studies indicate that this small species does not likely belong to in this genus and will likely be changed in the future.

Blewit *Lepista nuda*

Other Names
Wood blewit; formerly *Tricholoma nudum*, *Rhodopaxillus nudus* and *Clitocybe nuda*; incorrectly *Tricholoma personatum*.
Description
Scattered or in groups; often grows in a ring.
Spore Print: Pink. **Cap:** Lilac to brown; top convex to flat or slightly depressed, margin inrolled while young and often

lifts as the individual ages; surface smooth and often silvery, not sticky when moist. **Gills:** Lilac to brown when mature; crowded. **Stalk:** Bluish lilac with minute hairs; usually bulbous at base. **Veil:** Absent. **Size:** Cap to 6" (15 cm) across. Stalk to 3¼" (8 cm) long.
Season August to December; November to March in California.
Habitat On the ground, in areas of organic debris.
Range Europe; widespread in North America.
Edibility Edible and choice.
Notes This species is sold in European markets, where its common name came from. There it was called "blue hat," which was shortened to "blewit." This is a choice species, one of a very few purple mushroom species that are edible. It can be identified easily by a combina-

tion of characteristics, including an overall purple color, inrolled margin while young, powerful fruity fragrance, pink gills and lack of a veil. It tends to be abundant in areas where it grows; producing large numbers of excellent-tasting edible mushrooms. Blewits are cultivated in France and are therefore available commercially in Europe.

Similar Species Purple-staining Cortinarius *Cortinarius mutabilis*, similar to the blewit, but its spores are brown and it has a cobwebby veil.

Crowded White Clitocybe *Clitocybe dilatata*

Other Names Also known as *C. cerussata* var. *difformis*.
Description Densely clustered. **Spore Print:** White. **Cap:** Gray to white; convex to flat, often irregularly shaped; surface smooth and dry; flesh firm. **Gills:** White to buff; crowded. **Stalk:** Off-white; often thicker at base; fibrous. **Size:** Cap to 6" (15 cm) across. Stalk to 4¾" (12 cm) long.
Season September to November.
Habitat On the ground, in areas with gravel in the soil such as roadsides and trails.
Range Yukon, Pacific Northwest, New Mexico.
Edibility Poisonous.
Notes The tight clusters of this fleshy species, along with its irregularly shaped caps and gravelly habitat, are helpful in identification. It is reported that eating the crowded white clitocybe causes muscarine poisoning, whose symptoms

include profuse perspiration, tears, blurred vision, abdominal cramps and constricted pupils. In most cases these symptoms subside in 6 to 24 hours.

Clubfooted Clitocype *Clitocybe clavipes*

Other Names Club-foot, fat-footed clitocype.
Description Solitary or in small groups. **Spore Print:** White. **Cap:** Brownish; convex to flat maturing to depressed and eventually funnel-shaped; surface smooth. **Gills:** White to yellowish brown; crowded; decurrent (running down the stem). **Stalk:** Light brown; slender; base enlarged and covered with a white, cotton-like covering. **Size:** Cap to 4" (10 cm) across. Stalk to 2¾" (7 cm) long.
Season July to November; December to February in California.
Habitat On the ground, in mixed-woods and coniferous forests, especially pine.
Range Widely distributed in North America.
Edibility Rated by some authors as edible, but other similar-colored species are poisonous. Not recommended.

Notes Some individuals who consumed alcohol after eating the clubfooted clitocype have experienced coprine poisoning—similar to that experienced by those who consume alcohol with alcohol inky (see p. 41). Symptoms include headache, hot flashes, internal disturbances and a rash.

Large White Leucopaxillus *Leucopaxillus albissimus*

Other Name White leucopax.
Description Solitary to gregarious or in a ring. **Spore Print:** White. **Cap:** White, maturing to tan; convex to flat; margin inrolled when young; surface smooth and dry, dull finish; flesh very firm, thick. **Gills:** White to yellowish; crowded and narrow. **Stalk:** White; often thicker toward the base; covered with fine white mycelium (threads). **Size:** Cap to 16" (40 cm) across. Stalk to 8" (20 cm) long.
Season August to November.
Habitat On the ground, under conifers.
Range Widespread in North America.
Edibility Not palatable since it is very hard to digest. Not recommended.
Notes Large white leucopaxillus individuals are very tough and long-lived—often lasting a month or longer. The dense white mycelium that cements the old needles together is an important characteristic of this species. It's a pity that this species is not edible, since it is sweet-smelling and often grows in abundance.

 # Common Laccaria *Laccaria laccata*

Other Names Lackluster laccaria, deceiver.
Description Scattered or in small groups. **Spore Print:** White. **Cap:** Tawny to brick red; top convex to flat and eventually depressed, margin often uplifted; surface dry, not sticky. **Gills:** Pinkish to reddish tan; well spaced, somewhat waxy. **Stalk:** Tawny to reddish brown; slender. **Size:** Cap to 2¼" (6 cm) across. Stalk to 3¼" (8 cm) long.
Season June to November; through the winter in California.
Habitat On the ground under or near trees and in bogs. It often grows under pines and favors poor soils and sandy areas.
Range Worldwide. Throughout most of North America.
Edibility Edible, but the stems are often tough and should be discarded.
Notes The common laccaria is a beautiful species with pleasant colors and a wide variety of

cap shapes that often hold their shape for an extended time. The variability in appearance of specimens is the reason for one of its common names—deceiver. Specimens growing in bogs are said to have more fibrous stems, but they are also normally insect-free—a bonus for those interested in edible species. **Similar Species Bicoloured Laccaria** *Laccaria bicolor*, very similar, but the downy mycelium at the base of the stem is violet rather than white.

Western Amethyst Laccaria
Laccaria amethysteo-occidentalis

Other Names Western purple laccaria; formerly included in the *Laccaria amethystea* group.
Description Scattered or in small groups. **Spore Print:** White or tinged with lilac. **Cap:** Deep purple-violet fading to brown when old; top convex to flat and eventually depressed, margin often uplifted as it ages; surface may be scaly. **Gills:** Deep violet; adnexed (unattached); widely spaced. **Stalk:** Purple-violet; surface dry and striate (finely grooved or covered with lines); base woolly. **Size:** Cap to 3¼" (8 cm) across. Stalk to 4" (10 cm) long.
Season August to October.
Habitat On the ground, under mixed-woods and conifers.
Range Western North America.
Edibility Edible, but the hairy stems should be discarded.
Notes The western amethyst laccaria is distinctive; yet it occurs in a variety of shapes. Its rich color and handsome shapes make it an excellent photographic subject as well as an edible species. If you plan to gather them for eating, be sure to check the spore color to ensure it is the correct species.
Similar Species **Violet Cortinarius** *Cortinarius violaceus* (see p. 50)

Fried Chicken Mushroom *Lyophyllum decastes*

Other Names Clustered domecap; *L. multiceps, Clitocybe multiceps, Tricholoma aggregatum.*
Description Gregarious in compact groups. **Spore Print:** White. **Cap:** Gray to yellowish brown; convex to flat; margin often uplifted; surface smooth and slippery when moist; flesh firm. **Gills:** White; crowded; adnate (attached). **Stalk:** White; smooth and dry; often tapering downward; veil absent. **Size:** Cap to 4¾" (12 cm) across. Stalk to 4" (10 cm) long.
Season June to October; overwinters in California.
Habitat On the ground, in grassy areas and disturbed areas such as roads and trails.
Range Widely distributed in North America.
Edibility Edible, but there are a few reports of mild poisonings that could have been allergic reactions.
Notes Fried chicken mushroom is an edible species known for (and named for) its "fried chicken" taste. The flavour may be better described as crunchy and mild with a hint of seasoning—the seasoning you add to it! This is a plentiful species, however, and is easily

identified with its gregarious growing habits. To ensure you have collected this species and not another, check the color of the cap and spores, and the absence of a veil.
Similar Species **Clustered Clitocybe** *Clitocybe subconnexa*, a white fungus that also grows in clusters, but its spores are pinkish. **Crowded White Clitocybe** *Clitocybe dilatata* (see p. 22), yet another white species with white spores.

White Matsutake *Tricholoma magnivelare*

Other names
Matsutake, pine mushroom, American matsutake; formerly known as *Armillaria ponderosa*.

Description Scattered or in small groups. **Spore Print:** White. **Cap:** White and later yellowish to reddish brown fibres develop to form patches; margin inrolled and cottony at first; dry to slightly sticky when moist; flesh very firm and

thick. **Gills:** White to cinnamon with age. **Stalk:** White above the ring and scaly below; very firm. **Veil:** White; prominent and membranous; forms a cotton-like ring. **Size:** Cap to 14" (35 cm) across. Stalk to 6" (15 cm) long.

Season October, to December.

Habitat On the ground, under conifers.

Range Primarily the Pacific Northwest as well as much of northern North America.

Edibility Edible and choice.

Notes The white matsutake or pine mushroom is a firm, distinctive-looking species that has a spicy aroma not unlike cinnamon. The fragrant spicy scent of white matsutake is distinctive, as is its membranous veil.

    This world-renowned mushroom is commercially harvested in large numbers and shipped to Japan, where it is considered a delicacy. It has been estimated that the white matsutake harvest in Canada reaches 250,000 pounds (113 tonnes) annually, considerably more than in the United States. Its price fluctuates wildly from year to year, occasionally fetching as much as $200 per pound ($440/kg).

    This species often grows with the distinctive saprophytic wildflower candystick *Allotropa virgata*, a wildflower indicator species, or the booted knight *Tricholoma focale* (see p. 27), a mushroom indicator species.

Similar Species Fragrant Armillaria *Armillaria caligata*, a smaller edible species with large scales on the cap and dark patches on the stem. Its common name comes from its strong cinnamon aroma.

Smith's Amanita *Amanita smithiana* (see p. 33) (and others), various white-colored Amanita species in the button stage are often mistaken for small specimens of white matsutake. It is a serious error to identify Smith's amanita as an edible species—if it is eaten, it can cause kidney failure. **Extreme caution is advised.**

Honey Mushroom *Armillaria mellea* complex

Description Cespitose (many mushrooms emanate from a single point), or in troops. **Spore Print:** White. **Cap:** Yellowish brown to dark brown; bell-shaped or convex maturing to flat; surface covered with dark brown scales. **Gills:** White to yellowish, and darker on aging. **Stalk:** White, yellowish brown; surface often covered with scales; fibrous, not fracturing like a piece of chalk. **Veil:** Off-white to yellowish; membranous; forms a brown or brown-rimmed ring. **Size:** Cap to 6" (15 cm) across. Stalk to 8" (20 cm) long.
Season September to November.
Habitat On standing wood, buried wood or organic debris near the trunks of coniferous trees and occasionally on deciduous wood.

Range Circumpolar; throughout much of North America.
Edibility Edible, but the tough stems should be discarded. This mushroom has been reported to cause some people gastro-intestinal upset if collected from hemlock. Others believe that most of these reports are due to undercooking and overeating. It is easy to mistake honey mushrooms for other species, since they can be quite variable in appearance. **Caution is advised.**

Notes The name honey mushroom *Armillaria mellea* is applied to approximately 12 closely related species throughout North America. The common name of this species is derived from its color, rather than its taste! These mushrooms are favored for pickling as well as drying. The mycelia of the honey mushroom glow in the dark. Scientists are uncertain how this trait contributes to the health of the mushroom, though there is speculation that the light produced by the mycelia may attract insects, which help in spreading spores.

The honey mushroom has been identified as one of the largest living organisms in the world. In the Blue Mountains of eastern Oregon, researchers were astonished to find one fungus that covered over 2,200 acres (880 hectares)—the equivalent of about 1,665 football fields. The fungus was estimated to have been living for at least 2,400 years, possibly longer. The honey mushroom spreads by the use of black rhizomorphs (shoelace-like hyphae), which reach out from one tree to another. The only organism in the world considered to be larger is clones of the trembling aspen *Populus tremuloides*.

Man On Horseback *Tricholoma flavovirens*

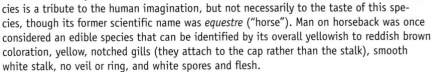

Other Names Canary trich; formerly *T. equestre*.
Description Scattered to gregarious. **Spore Print:**
White. **Cap:** Yellow to reddish brown with a yellowish edge; convex to flat; margin often uplifted as it ages; surface smooth, sticky when moist; flesh firm.
Gills: Yellowish; crowded, notched. **Stalk:** White to pale yellow; surface smooth and dry. **Veil:** Absent.
Size: Cap to 8" (20 cm) across. Stalk to 4" (10 cm) long.
Season August to November; October to January in California.
Habitat On the ground, in grassy areas under pines.
Range Widely distributed in North America.
Edibility Unknown. Once thought to be edible; however, there have been fatalities in France. **Do not eat**.
Notes The flamboyant common name of this species is a tribute to the human imagination, but not necessarily to the taste of this species, though its former scientific name was *equestre* ("horse"). Man on horseback was once considered an edible species that can be identified by its overall yellowish to reddish brown coloration, yellow, notched gills (they attach to the cap rather than the stalk), smooth white stalk, no veil or ring, and white spores and flesh.
Similar Species Deceiving Knight *Tricholoma sejunctum*, a yellow species with white gills and black fibers on the cap.
Sulphur Knight *Tricholoma sulphureum*, a yellow species with a strong, offensive odor.

Booted Knight *Tricholoma focale*

Other Names Zeller's tricholoma, fetid armillaria; *T. zelleri, Armillaria zelleri*.
Description Scattered to gregarious. **Spore Print:** White. **Cap:** Brownish orange; convex to flat or slightly umbonate (with a knob-like top); surface sticky when moist; veil remnants often hang from margin; flesh firm. **Gills:** White, stains rusty brown; crowded; adnate (attached). **Stalk:** White above ring, fibrous below; normally tapers toward base. **Veil:** White;

membranous, forms a ragged ring. **Size:** Cap to 6" (15 cm) across. Stalk to 5⅓" (13 cm) long.
Season July to August in northern regions of North America; December to February in California.
Habitat On the ground in coniferous and deciduous forests, especially pine.
Range Widespread in North America, especially Pacific Northwest.
Edibility Not edible.
Notes In some years this species is very common. It often grows in the same area as the white matsutake (see p. 25). This information can sometimes help in locating the prized white matsutake.

Fairy Ring Mushroom *Marasmius oreades*

Description In small groups, or rings. **Spore Print:** White. **Cap:** Tan to light brown; bell-shaped maturing to umbonate; margin often uplifted as it ages; surface smooth and dry; flesh rather tough. **Gills:** White to tan; well spaced and broad. **Stalk:** Tan or lighter; slender and of uniform thickness. **Size:** Cap to 2⅓" (6 cm) across. Stalk to 3¼" (8 cm) long. **Season** May to November, throughout the year in California.

Habitat On the ground, in lawns, fields and similar open areas.

Range Throughout North America.

Edibility Edible and choice, but ensure you have the correct species. The tough stems are often discarded.

Notes This familiar species sometimes smells like almonds but more often produces an unidentifiable pleasant scent. It can kill a lawn with its nutritional requirements. Many other species of mushrooms grow in lawns, some of which also form rings or partial rings and may be poisonous.

The fairy ring mushroom is easily dried, and rehydrates nicely to a near fresh condition. It is great in soups, stews and gravies, and some have suggested that it can be used as a substitute for white matsutake or pine mushrooms (see p. 25) in certain recipes. Be sure that the area where you harvest this species is free from herbicides and fungicides before picking.

The key features by which this species can be identified correctly in a lawn are white spores, umbonate cap, well-spaced white to buff gills and thin, tough stems. Ask a mushroom expert to be sure.

Similar Species Sweat-producing Clitocybe *Clitocybe dealbata*, a small, grayish white mushroom with white spores and close gills that often grows in grassy areas. It was named for the common effects of eating it—tremendous sweating, along with salivation and diarrhea. This nondescript species is sometimes misidentified as the fairy ring mushroom, an error that can be fatal to young children.

Common Conifer Cystoderma *Cystoderma fallax*

Other Names Conifer cystoderma, deceptive grainy cap.
Description Solitary to small groups. **Spore Print:**
White. **Cap:** Rusty orange to brown; top convex to flat or
umbonate (with a knob-like top); margin often with veil
remnants; surface dry with minute granules. **Gills:** White;
narrow and crowded. **Stalk:** Similar to cap color above
ring; of uniform thickness or thicker at base; surface
smooth above ring and granular below. **Veil:** Forms a
flared ring that is persistent and similar to cap color.
Size: Cap to 2" (5 cm) across. Stalk to 2¾" (7 cm) long.
Season September to October.
Habitat On the ground, in mixed-woods and coniferous
forests; also on rotting wood.
Range Pacific Northwest, Rocky Mountains.
Edibility Not edible.
Notes The common conifer cystoderma is a distinctive
species with a sock-like sheath that extends from the
ring to the base. This species is also found around the
Great Lakes region.
Similar Species **Earthy Powdercap** *Cystoderma amianthinum*, a common species that is
similar overall, with a very slim ring on the stalk.

Pleated Marasmius *Marasmius plicatulus*

Other Name Velvet-cap marasmius.
Description Scattered to gregarious.
Spore Print: White. **Cap:** Brown;
bell-shaped or conical maturing to
convex or flat; pleated; surface dry,
velvet-like; flesh thin. **Gills:** White to
pinkish; well-spaced. **Stalk:** Chestnut, lighter at the top; smooth; long,
slender and of uniform thickness.
Size: Cap to 2" (5 cm) across. Stalk
to 5⅓" (13 cm) long.
Season September to October; November to February in California.
Habitat On the ground, in various
forests.
Range Western North America.
Edibility Not edible.
Notes The pleated marasmius is
truly a handsome species with its
rich, red-brown velvet-like cap and
light-colored gills. This species is
believed to be endemic to the Pacific
Northwest.

Fircone Cap *Strobilurus trullisatus*

Other Names Douglas-fir collybia; also known as *S. kemptonae*, *Collybia trullisata*.
Description In small groups. **Spore Print:** White. **Cap:** White or pinkish; convex to flat or slightly depressed as it ages; surface dry; flesh fragile. **Gills:** White. **Stalk:** White; slender. **Size:** Cap to ⅝" (1.5 cm) across. Stalk to 2" (5 cm) long.
Season August to November.
Habitat On the cones of the Douglas-fir and occasionally other conifers.
Range Western North America.
Edibility Unknown, and too small to be of any value.

Notes This remarkable fungus only grows on old cones fallen from conifers. Several different species may be found, each having a favourite species of cone to live on. Other fungi such as *Mycena* spp. may also grow on fallen cones, but they are not restricted to them.

 # Wood Woollyfoot *Collybia peronata*

Other Name Also known as *Marasmius peronatus*.
Description Scattered or in small groups.
Spore Print: White. **Cap:** Light brown to reddish ochre; top convex to flat or slightly umbonate. **Gills:** Cream to yellow; widely spaced and large. **Stalk:** Yellowish brown; resilient, densely covered at base with white to yellowish hairs. **Size:** Cap to 6" (15 cm) across. Stalk to 3¼" (8 cm) long.
Season August to November.
Habitat On the ground, among leaf litter and occasionally coniferous needles.
Range Europe and throughout much of North America.
Edibility Rated poisonous by some authorities and inedible by others because of its peppery taste.
Notes Recent research in Europe has shown that this species is important in its ability to break down the upper 1½" (4 cm) of leaf litter on the forest floor. The distinctive hairs on its stem makes it particularly easy to identify.

Clustered Collybia *Gymnopus acervatus*

Other Name Also known as *Collybia acervata*.
Description Several to gregarious. **Spore Print:**
White. **Cap:** Reddish brown to pinkish brown; convex; surface smooth; forms tufts; flesh very thin and fragile. **Gills:** White or pink to buff; crowded and narrow. **Stalk:** Brown; slender and equal; hollow. **Size:** Cap to 2" (5 cm) across. Stalk to 4¾" (12 cm) long.
Season July to October.
Habitat Adjacent to or growing on rotting conifers.
Range Rocky Mountains, Pacific Northwest and northern California.
Edibility Not edible. It is also believed to be slightly poisonous to some people.
Notes The clustered collybia is an easily identified visual treat to find in the woods. Its long, delicate stems curve in symmetry with others from their common origin make a truly wonderful woodland display.

Lichen Agaric *Omphalina ericetorum*

Other Names Also known as *O. umbellifera, Gerronema ericetorum*.
Description Solitary or in small groups. **Spore Print:** White or yellow. **Cap:** Brown to yellow; flat with an incurved margin to funnel-shaped as it ages; margin wavy; surface smooth; flesh resilient. **Gills:** Yellowish; decurrent (running down the stem). **Stalk:** Brown to yellow; smooth or with tiny scales; slender and may be thicker at base; surface smooth. **Size:** Cap to 1⅓" (3.5 cm) across. Stalk to 1⅛" (3 cm) long.

Season June to September; March to May and October to November along the Pacific coast.
Habitat On rotted wood when a green alga *Coccomyxa* sp. is present.
Range Europe; throughout northern North America.
Edibility Not edible.
Notes The genus name *Omphalina* means "possessing a navel"—an excellent description for this group. The lichen agaric is the first species to be seen in the spring and most common species of gilled mushroom found in the Arctic. It forms a lichen-like association with a green alga *Coccomyxa* sp., much like the associations with trees formed by so many other mushroom species. Thus the common name lichen agaric is also very appropriate.

Bleeding Mycena *Mycena haematopus*

Other Names Bleeding fairy helmet, blood-foot mushroom.
Description Solitary or clustered. **Spore Print:** White. **Cap:** Reddish pink to reddish brown; convex to conical maturing to flat; margin often uplifted as it ages; surface dry; flesh fragile. **Gills:** White to pink; adnate (attached). **Stalk:** Red to reddish brown; smooth; slender; coarse hairs at base. **Size:** Cap to 2" (5 cm) across. Stalk to 5½" (14 cm) long.
Season April to November.
Habitat On decaying stumps, trunks and logs.
Range Throughout North America.
Edibility Unknown. Eating is not recommended.
Notes This common species obtained its common name from the characteristic oozing of a dark red fluid from its flesh where broken. In young specimens, the cap margin clasps to the stem in the shape of a cylinder. When mature, this species normally displays tiny tooth-like projections along the margin, which aid in identifying this species.

Scarlet Mycena *Mycena adonis*

Other Names Scarlet bonnet; *M. amabilissima, M. roseipallens, M. roseocandida* and *M. fusipes*.
Description Scattered or in small groups. **Spore Print:** White. **Cap:** Scarlet fading to yellow or white; conical to flat, shallow grooves may be present; flesh fragile. **Gills:** Pink fading to white. **Stalk:** Pink to orange; slender and of uniform thickness; often downy at base. **Size:** Cap to ½" (12 mm) across. Stalk to 1⅓" (3.5 cm) long.
Season June to September.
Habitat On the needles of coniferous trees.
Range Pacific Northwest, northern California.
Edibility Too small to be of any value.
Notes Additional research is required on the many species of *Mycena* found in the Northwest. The scarlet mycena is thought to be the same species as several similar species identified by researchers. Other authors believe that there are indeed several species of very similar-looking reddish mycena. This seems to be another example of the age-old difference between splitters and lumpers. Only more research will determine who is right. Meanwhile, enjoy the wonderful color of this species or species complex.

Deer Mushroom *Pluteus cervinus*

Other Names Fawn mushroom, fawn-colored pluteus; formerly *P. atricapillus*.

Description Solitary or in small groups. **Spore Print:** Pink. **Cap:** Grayish brown to dark brown; convex to flat or slightly umbonate surface sticky when moist, flesh soft and white. **Gills:** White turning pink at maturity, dark fibrils; free when mature. **Stalk:** White to light brown; dark fibrils. **Veil:** Absent. **Size:** Cap to 6" (15 cm) across. Stalk to 5⅓" (13 cm) long.

Season Throughout the year, depending upon the area.

Habitat On decaying deciduous wood or sawdust, rarely on conifers.

Range Throughout North America.

Edibility Edible but not highly regarded.

Notes The deer mushroom is a handsome species that is commonly encountered in the woods. Its odor is faintly radish-like. Some poisonous mushrooms (*Entoloma* sp.) can easily be mistaken for the deer mushroom. To be safe, collect only those that have dark fibrils on a white stem and free gills, and those that are definitely growing on wood.

Smith's Amanita *Amanita smithiana*

Description Solitary or in small groups. **Spore Print:** White. **Cap:** White with cotton-like warts, top convex to flat. **Gills:** White to cream-colored. **Stalk:** White; ragged, thickening toward base. **Partial Veil:** White and cotton-like; shaggy cotton-like veil remnant on young specimens, leaves a fragile, ragged ring on the stalk that easily falls off. **Universal Veil:** White to light brown. **Size:** Cap to 5" (12.5 cm) across. Stalk to 8" (20 cm) long.

Season September to October.

Habitat On the ground, under conifers.

Range Pacific Northwest and northern California.

Edibility **Poisonous**, often causing kidney failure.

Notes Smith's amanita is a common species along the Pacific coast. The cotton-like partial veil is quite remarkable when the mushroom is in its younger stage. This species has an unpleasant odor that has been described as chlorine-like. It is sometimes mistaken for the white matsutake (see p. 25). Several poisonings have resulted from people gathering this amanita, in the belief that they were picking the white matsutake.

Cotton-like veil.

Death Cap *Amanita phalloides*

Other Name Death cup.

Description Solitary, scattered or in small groups. **Spore Print:** White. **Cap:** Green to brownish olive, often with a metallic luster; top convex to flat; smooth, tacky when moist. **Gills:** White, occasionally tinged with green. **Stalk:** White, greenish or brownish; smooth or with tiny scales. **Partial Veil:** White to yellowish green; membranous, forms a fragile, skirt-like ring. **Universal Veil:** White; membranous, forms a volva (bulb) that is normally buried. Button resembles a puffball; be sure to section all puffballs to ensure they do not have a stalk, cap and gills. **Size:** Cap to 6⅓" (16 cm) across. Stalk to 7" (18 cm) long.

Season July to November; occasionally to January in California.

Habitat On the ground, under various trees; in both western and eastern North America under oaks, as well as other hardwoods and pines.

Range Southern B.C. to California; rare north of Oregon.

Edibility Deadly poisonous. Incidentally, it is said to taste excellent by those who have tasted it and survived!

Notes Introduced from Europe, this species is the most deadly mushroom known. A single specimen can kill a human being, and 90% of all fatal mushroom-poisoning incidents in Europe have been attributed to this species. Symptoms take 6 to 24 hours to become evident. Death cap causes irreparable damage to the liver and kidneys. Although there is no antidote, treatment has improved in recent years—it often includes an organ transplant.

This mushroom often fruits in parks, where it forms mycorrhiza with ornamental trees or shrubs. Its odor changes with time, from a mild scent like that of rose petals to a pungent, chlorine-like smell or that of raw potatoes or old honey. The most distinctive odor, however, is the rotting-meat smell of older specimens.

The button stage of this species, and all amanitas, closely resemble puffballs. It is imperative to check any mushroom, including puffballs, by slicing it in half to ensure that it is not the button stage of an amanita.

Similar Species Destroying Angel *Amanita virosa*, an all-white species with a scaly stalk and very poisonous properties. Destroying angel is especially common in eastern North America and has also been reported in the Pacific Northwest. It has been responsible for many poisonings and deaths throughout North America. Emperor Claudius, who ruled Rome 2,000 years ago, was the earliest known victim of this species' poison.

Panther Amanita *Amanita pantherina*

Other Names Panther, panther cap.
Description Solitary or scattered. **Spore Print:** White. **Cap:**
Yellowish brown to dark brown with white wart patches; convex to flat or slightly depressed; surface sticky when moist.
Gills: White; closely spaced. Stalk: White to cream. Ring near top of stem; volva prominent and white; oval with a wooly edge. **Partial Veil:** White, with ragged or toothed margin; a prominent ring is produced. **Universal Veil:** White, forms a collar-like volva. **Size:** Cap to 10" (25 cm) across. Stalk to 8" (20 cm) long.
Season September and October; to spring in California.
Habitat On the ground, under deciduous and coniferous trees, especially Douglas-fir.
Range Rocky Mountains west to the coast, rare in the East.
Edibility Poisonous. This species is one of the most common causes of mushroom poisoning in the Pacific Northwest.
Notes The panther amanita got its name from the white spots (veil remnants) on a brown background, like the markings of the feline. It is a common mushroom in the Pacific Northwest, so all those who pick mushrooms should be aware of its poisonous properties. The symptoms include delirium, vomiting, raving and a coma-like sleep.

Gemmed Amanita *Amanita gemmata*

Other Names Jonquil amanita; also known as *Amanita junquillea*.
Description Solitary to small groups. **Spore Print:** White. **Cap:** Yellow to cream-colored with white warts; top convex to flat or slightly depressed.
Gills: White, closely spaced. **Stalk:** White, often tinged with yellow; dry, smooth above the ring and sometimes scaly below; often with a prominent enlarged base. **Partial Veil:** Normally present, white, membranous, forming a skirt-like ring. **Universal Veil:** Present, white, forming a collar-like volva.
Size: Cap to 5½" (14 cm) across. Stalk to 5⅓" (13 cm) long.
Season June to October; November to February in California.
Habitat On the ground, in mixed woods and coniferous forests.
Range North America, most common in the West.
Edibility Poisonous.
Notes In northern regions of the Pacific Northwest, this species fruits once the first rains of autumn are upon us. The gemmed amanita often hybridizes with the panther amanita (see above). The results are mushrooms that display characteristics of both species.

Fly Amanita *Amanita muscaria*

Other Name Fly agaric.
Description Solitary to small groups and in large rings.
Spore Print: White. **Cap:** Blood red to yellow; convex to flat; surface sticky when moist; remnants of volva are often in concentric circles.
Gills: White, crowded and swollen, free, closely spaced and broad. **Stalk:** White to cream with scales; hollow to stuffed; ring present at top of stem; remnant of volva is visible as a shallow rim on upper portion of basal bulb. **Partial Veil:** White, may be present or absent, membranous. **Universal Veil:** Cream-colored, covered with white warts, bulb with 2–4 concentric rings. **Size:** Cap to 16" (40 cm) across. Stalk to 12" (30 cm) long.
Season June to November, winter in California.

Habitat On the ground, in or near forests of pine, spruce, fir, birch and aspen.

Range Circumpolar. Found in much of North America, most commonly in the Pacific Northwest.

Edibility Poisonous with hallucinogenic properties. The drying process changes ibotenic acid into muscimol, the agent responsible for its hallucinogenic properties and for symptoms such as nausea, vomiting and diarrhea.

Notes Fly amanita is a very common species that is quite exciting to find for the first time. Its common name likely comes from its historical use as a fly killer. Small pieces of dried mushroom are placed in a bowl of milk. Flies are attracted to a chemical compound in the flesh of this mushroom that intoxicates them. They fall into the milk and drown, or die from the poisons they have consumed. The active ingredient of this "insecticide" has been identified as ibotenic acid.

Fly amanita can also cause death in humans and is believed to have been a favorite poison in ancient Rome. However, in small doses it has also been used in homeopathic medicine to calm nervous spasms. It was also commonly used as a hallucinogenic in Russia and Europe prior to the use of alcohol.

This brightly colored species is also known for its ability to concentrate vanadium, a rare metal used to strengthen steel.

Several color varieties of this mushroom also occur in the Pacific Northwest. The bright red-capped variety (var. *muscaria*) is the coloration most commonly encountered, but a yellow-capped variety (var. *formosa*) can also be found. A grayish-white capped variety (var. *alba*) may also be discovered, especially in northern areas. All varieties have the characteristic warts on the cap unless rain has washed them off.

Amanita muscaria var. *formosa*

Constricted Grisette *Amanita constricta*

Description Solitary, scattered or in small groups. **Spore Print:** White. **Cap:** Gray to brown, often with a patch of white to gray universal veil; top convex to flat; grooved cap margin. **Gills:** White to gray. **Stalk:** Gray; smooth or with tiny scales. **Partial Veil:** Absent. **Universal Veil:** White to gray or buff; forms a flaring volva with a constriction around the stalk. **Size:** Cap to 5⅓" (13 cm) across. Stalk to 6½" (16 cm) long.

Season August to November.

Habitat On the ground, in coniferous and hardwood forests.

Range Alaska to California.

Edibility Edible. However, caution should be exercised, because this mushroom looks similar to at least two poisonous species. If you do wish to eat it, never collect buttons or younger specimens, which may be poisonous.

Notes Constricted grisette is a common species in the Pacific Northwest as well as eastern North America. It is a member of the Amanita group, which have grooves along the cap margin. This species is easily identified with a constricted or pinched volva and lack of a partial veil or ring on the stalk.

Shaggy Parasol *Lepiota rachodes*

Other Names Also known as *Macrolepiota rachodes*, *Leucoagaricus rachodes*; occasionally spelt *Lepiota rhacodes*.

Description Normally in groups or rings. **Spore Print:** White. **Cap:** Brown; top convex to flat or slightly umbonate (knob-like) at maturity; surface covered with shaggy scales; margin fringed; flesh firm and thick. **Gills:** White; free; closely spaced. **Stalk:** White to brown; surface smooth, thicker at the base or with a basal bulb; dry. **Veil:** White or edged in brown; membranous; forms a double-edged collar-like ring. **Size:** Cap to 8" (20 cm) across. Stalk to 7" (18 cm) long.

Season September to October; November to February in California.

Habitat On the ground, in forests, especially conifers, as well as disturbed areas, roadsides and similar sites.

Range Throughout North America.

Edibility Edible and choice; however, some people develop intestinal problems after eating this species.

Notes The flesh of the shaggy parasol stains orange, changing to reddish, when it is cut. Individuals who have tried this species remark on its strong nutty flavor. If you wish to eat it, sauté it on a high heat, uncovered, which is believed to reduce the chances of gastro-intestinal upset.

Similar Species Green-spored Parasol *Chlorophyllum molybdites*, a poisonous species that is similar overall, with an off-white color. It produces a green spore print and grows on lawns and open areas in rings or groups. It is found in southern United States including California.

Shaggy-stalked Parasol *Lepiota clypeolaria*

Other Names Shaggy-stalked lepiota, shield dapperling.
Description Solitary or in small groups. **Spore Print:**
White. **Cap:** Yellow-brown to brown, darker in the center;
bell-shaped to convex or slightly umbonate (central
knob); center smooth, margin shaggy, cotton-like. **Gills:**
White or creamy; crowded; free. **Stalk:** Yellowish brown;
ring is absent, covered in cottony scales below veil. **Partial Veil:** White; leaves cotton-like remnants on margin.
Size: Cap to 3¼" (8 cm) across. Stalk to 7" (18 cm) long.
Season September to November; November to February in
California.
Habitat On the ground, in coniferous and deciduous
forests.
Range Widely distributed in North America.
Edibility Poisonous.
Notes The shaggy-stalked parasol is a common species
that appears in a wide variety of woodland settings. The
combination of a shaggy cotton-like cap and stalk along
with a smooth cap center, white or cream-colored gills
and the lack of a ring help to distinguish this handsome species.

Black-eyed Parasol *Lepiota atrodisca*

Other Name Black-disk lepiota.
Description Solitary or in small
groups. **Spore Print:** White. **Cap:**
White with black or gray central
scales; convex to flat or slightly
depressed; margin often uplifted as
it ages; surface dry; flesh fragile.
Gills: White; crowded and narrow;
free. **Stalk:** Off-white; smooth; of
uniform thickness or thicker at base.
Partial Veil: White, membranous;
forms a sleeve-like ring. **Size:** Cap
to 2" (5 cm) across. Stalk to 3" (7.5
cm) long.
Season October to November; November to February in California.
Habitat On the ground or in decaying deciduous or coniferous wood.
Range Pacific Northwest, California.
Edibility Unknown, and because others in this group are deadly, it's not worth testing.
Notes This small, dainty-looking parasol easily goes undetected in the forest understory.
The overall nondescript color, along with gray or black scales in the central area of the cap,
are its key identification marks.

Meadow Mushroom *Agaricus campestris*

Other Name Field mushroom.
Description Various sized groups or rings. **Spore Print:** Chocolate brown. **Cap:** White; dome-like or convex to flat; surface dry; flesh firm and stains slightly pinkish. **Gills:** Pink maturing to chocolate brown; crowded; free. **Stalk:** White; smooth above veil, fibrous scales often below. **Partial Veil:** White; evanescent (temporary) or leaves remnants on margin. **Size:** Cap to 6" (15 cm) across. Stalk to 4" (10 cm) long.

Season June to October.
Habitat On the ground, in open fields, pastures and similar grassy areas.
Range Woldwide; Alaska, Pacific Northwest and California.
Edibility Edible and choice. Several similar-looking poisonous species may also be encountered in similar habitats (see below). **Caution is advised.**
Notes This is one of the most commonly picked species of edible mushroom in the world. It is easily identified by its pink-staining flesh, a ring that consists of a single layer of tissue that often disappears completely, and dark chocolate spores. Under the right conditions, including moisture, this species can be very abundant. The meadow mushroom is excellent eating—raw in salads, sautéed in a skillet or added to a side dish.
Similar Species **Various Amanitas** *Amanita* spp., includes several poisonous species in their early growth stages, all with white spores and a volva (bulb). **Some are deadly! Caution is advised.**
Ma'am on Motorcycle *Lepiota naucina*, a white parasol mushroom with a bulb, ring, white free gills and white spores. This is an edible species but it has caused some folks to become ill and is very easily confused with several poisonous amanitas. **Do not eat.**
Green-spored Parasol *Chlorophyllum molybdites,* a large species with white to yellowish gills and green spores. This mushroom, commonly found on lawns and similar areas, is **poisonous.** It causes gastro-intestinal distress in most people and is very often the cause of mushroom poisoning in the United States. It is found in southern United States, including California.

Prince *Agaricus augustus*

Description Solitary or in small groups. **Spore Print:** Chocolate brown. **Cap:** Off-white to buff or ochre at maturity, stains yellow; normally "mushroom-shaped" or convex to flat, margin often uplifted as it ages; surface covered with brown fibrillose scales; flesh firm and thick. **Gills:** Pallid to grayish brown, maturing to chocolate brown; crowded; free. **Stalk:** White or yellowish; surface smooth above ring, brown-edged scales below, with a sheath; often thicker at base; normally positioned deep in soil. **Veil:** White to brown; cotton-like, membranous; forms a large, permanent double skirt-like ring (which does not disappear, as in the meadow mushroom). **Size:** Cap to 16" (40 cm) across. Stalk to 14" (35 cm) long.

Season July to October; year round in California.
Habitat On the ground, in clearings, roadsides and in the woods, especially under conifers.
Range Pacific Northwest, California.
Edibility Edible and choice.
Notes The sweet scent of almond accompanies this much sought-after species. Its prominent and permanent ring, together with its large size, chocolate-brown spores, shaggy stem (when young) and almond fragrance help to identify it.

  This species is a true prince of a mushroom—it provides a meal fit for a prince. Insect larvae like this mushroom, though, and often reach it before you even see it. Good hunting and good luck!
Similar Species Yellow-staining Agaricus *Agaricus xanthodermus*, a poisonous species that can be identified by its free gills, prominent whitish ring, unpleasant phenolic odor and its distinctive yellow-staining where it is cut or bruised.

Western Flat-top Agaricus *Agaricus praeclaresquamosus*

Other Names Flat-topped agaricus; *A. meleagris*.
Description Solitary, clustered or in small groups. **Spore Print:** Chocolate brown. **Cap:** Off-white; marshmallow-shaped to broadly convex and eventually flat; surface dry with grayish-brown fibrils; flesh firm, thick. **Gills:** Pallid maturing to blackish brown; free when mature; crowded. **Stalk:** White; smooth; base usually stains bright yellow when cut; skirt-like ring on upper portion. **Veil:** White; membranous, felt-like; forms a fragile skirt-like ring. **Size:** Cap to 10" (25 cm) across. Stalk to 7" (18 cm) long.
Season September to November; September to March in California.
Habitat On the ground, in forests as well as lawns and grassy areas.
Range Throughout western North America.
Edibility **Poisonous** to many folks, causing vomiting and diarrhea.
Notes The western flat-top agaricus has a strong, unpleasant smell that is often phenolic (creosote-like). Those who have tried it say that it tastes metallic. These characteristics certainly reinforce the poisonous rating of this species. Please note that this is not true for all poisonous mushrooms—some of them are actually very tasty.

Alcohol Inky *Coprinus atramentarius*

Other Names Common inkcap, inky cap, tippler's bane.
Description Scattered to small groups or clusters. **Spore Print:** Black. **Cap:** Tan to grayish brown; oval to bell-shaped and slightly depressed as it ages; surface smooth or with silky fibrils; flesh soft and thin. **Gills:** White to lavender gray and finally inky black; free. **Stalk:** White to pink and eventually black; smooth or with tiny scales; hollow. **Partial Veil:** Fibrous. **Size:** Cap to 3¼" (8 cm) across. Stalk to 6¾" (17 cm) long.

Season May to September; November to April in California.
Habitat On the ground, in cultivated areas such as lawns and gardens, as well as on old stumps.
Range Throughout North America.
Edibility Edible, but see cautions below.
Notes Alcohol inky gets its name from a complication that occurs when a person drinks alcoholic beverages within two days of eating this mushroom. The mushroom deactivates an enzyme that removes the alcohol's toxins from the blood, causing temporary illness and leaving the person vulnerable to alcohol poisoning. This effect lasts a couple of hours before the mushroom's effects dissipate. Symptoms may include flushing on the neck and face, nausea, headache, stomach cramps and tingling fingers. They can be very severe. This species has been used in the treatment of alcoholism.

Shaggy Mane *Coprinus comatus*

Other Names Shaggy inky cap, shaggy inkcap, lawyer's wig.
Description Solitary to gregarious. **Spore Print:** Black. **Cap:** White with a brown center; cylindrical to flat as the margin curls; surface not sticky, large white and brown scales; flesh soft. **Gills:** White to pink and finally black; crowded; free. **Stalk:** White; smooth. **Partial Veil:** White, membranous; forms an inferior ring that falls off. **Size:** Cap to 2¾" (7 cm) across. Stalk to 8" (20 cm) long.
Season May to June; September to November.
Habitat On hard ground, in grassy areas and similar sites; very common along roadsides, trails and disturbed areas.
Range Throughout northern hemisphere.
Edibility Edible and choice when prime.
Notes Shaggy mane is common and plentiful and one of the first mushrooms that many folks learn to identify. Its large scales and cylindrical shape, which expands to a bell shape, are characteristic.

A prominent chef has ranked this species as one of the best edible species available year round in France. It can be used in soups, marinades, gravy, salads, stews and other dishes. This species can be short-lived, popping up overnight. Depending upon conditions, it can enter its inedible "inky stage" within days. A distinctive species that is also known for its ability to push up through asphalt, this mushroom is now widespread, having been introduced to many areas where it did not grow naturally.

This specimen is turning inky.

Glistening Inkcap *Coprinus micaceus*

Other Names Mica cap, common inky cap.
Description Normally gregarious. **Spore Print:** Dark brown to black. **Cap:** Yellowish brown; top oval to bell-shaped and eventually convex; minute glistening particles (from universal veil) may be present; radiating grooves to margin. **Gills:** Off-white to gray and eventually black; crowded and narrow. **Stalk:** White to buff. **Partial Veil:** Absent or rudimentary. **Size:** Cap to 2" (5 cm) across. Stalk to 4¾" (12 cm) long.
Season April to October; year round in California.
Habitat On stumps and other wood debris.
Range Throughout North America.
Edibility Edible.

Notes The glistening mica-like particles found on the caps of this mushroom are easily washed off in the rains and so are not always present. Clusters of this species often contain large numbers of individuals. Like so many other mushrooms, this is actually a complex of several species.

Wooly Inkcap *Coprinus lagopus*

Other Names Wooly-stalked coprinus, hare's foot coprinus, hare's foot ink cap.
Description Solitary to large groups. **Spore Print:** Black. **Cap:** Grayish aging to black; top oval changing to flat, margin often uplifted as it ages; surface dry, with fine grayish hairs; flesh soft and thin. **Gills:** Gray to black; crowded and narrow; free. **Stalk:** White; covered in minute white hairs; hollow. **Partial Veil:** Absent. **Size:** Cap to 2⅓" (6 cm) across. Stalk to 8" (20 cm) long.
Season July to October; October to February in California.
Habitat In leaf litter, compost, woody debris and burnt areas.
Range Cosmopolitan.
Edibility Unknown.
Notes The wooly inkcap is a fragile, short-lived mushroom, whose fruiting bodies last only a few hours. Since it fruits for such a short period, it is likely more common than generally observed. It is believed that this beautiful species is actually several very similar species in a complex, rather than just one. More research is required.

● Bell-shaped Panaeolus *Panaeolus campanulatus*

Other Names Bell-cap panaeolus, bell mottlegill.
Description Solitary or in small groups. **Spore Print:** Black.
Cap: Gray or brown maturing to black; bell-shaped or conical;
surface smooth, shiny when dry; white veil remnants often
remain on margin. **Gills:** Same as cap; mottled due to spores
maturing at different times; crowded. **Stalk:** Gray to brown;
slender; brittle. **Veil:** Evanescent (temporary). **Size:** Cap to
1½" (4 cm) across. Stalk to 6" (15 cm) long.
Season June to November; year round in California.
Habitat In cow or horse pastures.
Range Widespread in North America.
Edibility Hallucinogenic. Not recommended. See notes below.
Notes The bell-shaped panaeolus is a handsome species that
grows on dung. This common species contains trace amounts
of psilocybin as well as serotonin (a natural mood-altering
chemical) and ibonetic acid (a chemical that causes nausea).
When large quantities of certain strains of this panaeolus are

eaten raw, mild hallucinogenic effects may occur, but in most cases none are felt. There are
other similar species of *Panaeolus* as well, some of which are poisonous. The mottled gills,
due to spores maturing at different times, are characteristic of *Panaeolus* species.

● Potent Psilocybe *Psilocybe cyanescens*

Other Name Bluing psilocybe.
Description Scattered to small groups. **Spore
Print:** Purple-brown to black. **Cap:** Chestnut brown
to yellow, often bluish staining near margin as
it dries out; convex to almost flat; margin often
wavy; surface smooth, tacky. **Gills:** Cinnamon
brown; attached. **Stalk:** White; occasionally
enlarged at base; bruises blue. **Partial Veil:** White.
Size: Cap to 2" (5 cm) across. Stalk to 3¼" (8 cm)
long.
Season September to November.
Habitat On coniferous wood chips.
Range Pacific Northwest to northern California.
Edibility Hallucinogenic.
Notes Potent psilocybe commonly grows on the
mulch used in gardens and landscaping. This species, which contains both psilocybin and psilocin,
is rated as a strong hallucinogenic when consumed
in larger amounts.
Similar Species Galerinas *Galerina* spp. See
Liberty Cap, Similar Species (p. 45).

Liberty Cap *Psilocybe semilanceata*

Other Names Magic Mushroom; formerly *Panaeolus semilanceata*.
Description Solitary or in small groups. **Spore Print:** Purple-brown. **Cap:** Chestnut brown to tan, often bluish staining on margin; finely striated margin, conical, bell-shaped often umbonate (knob-like), sticky when moist. **Gills:** Pallid fading to purple-brown. **Stalk:** White, brown or bluish; very slender and frequently curved. **Veil:** Absent or short-lived. **Size:** Cap to 1" (2.5 cm) across. Stalk to 4" (10 cm) long.
Season August to November.
Habitat In pastures, tall grass, lawns, sedges and similar sites.
Range Along coastlines worldwide; Pacific Northwest to northern California; west of the Cascades.
Edibility Hallucinogenic properties containing the active agents psilocybin and psilocin.
Notes This mushroom is one of the better-known hallucinogenic species of the Pacific Northwest. It is known to cause delirium and colorful visions for most people.

Liberty cap does not grow on dung, but rather in tall grass and sedges. The flesh and stalk of this species turns blue when bruised. A key feature of all members of the *Psilocybe* group is a sticky pellicle (skin-like covering) that is easily peeled from the cap when moist. This species often grows next to bell-shaped panaeolus (see p. 44).
Similar Species Cone Heads *Conocybe* spp., a group that includes deadly species, with caps that are conical, bell-shaped or occasionally convex, growing on dung and in various grassy habitats. The spore print is rusty brown to cinnamon-brown or ochre; however, the cap color varies with species.
Galerinas *Galerina* spp., a deadly group with a cap that is convex to flat or slightly umbonate and a surface that is smooth, with one of several colors. Habitat varies considerably and includes grassy areas and lawns. The rusty brown spore print is distinctive.

Questionable Stropharia *Stropharia ambigua*

Other Name Fringed ringstalk.

Description Solitary or in small groups. **Spore Print:** Dark purplish brown. **Cap:** Yellow to yellowish brown; convex to flat, margin may be uplifted as it ages; surface sticky or slimy when moist; margin with cotton-like veil remnants; flesh thick and soft. **Gills:** Gray darkening to purplish black; crowded and narrow; adnate (attached). **Stalk:** White; smooth above ring, cotton-like scales below; slender. **Veil:** White; cotton-like; remnants often left on margin or on stalk. **Size:** Cap to 6" (15 cm) across. Stalk to 7" (18 cm) long.

Season August to November.

Habitat On the ground, in deciduous or coniferous forests.

Range Pacific Northwest, northern California.

Edibility Unknown, but tastes like "old leaves" according to one account.

Notes Questionable stropharia, like all other members of the Stropharia family, is a saprophyte (it feeds on dead organic matter). It is a striking and easily identified member of the *Stropharia* clan. It appears in the springtime elsewhere in North America.

Similar Species Gemmed Amanita *Amanita gemmata* (see p. 35), with a similar-colored cap, but white spores and often with a prominent volva (bulb).

Lacerated Stropharia *Stropharia hornemannii*

Other Names Conifer roundhead, luxuriant ringstalk; also known as *Stropharia depilata*.

Description Solitary and in small groups. **Spore Print:** Purple to purplish black. **Cap:** Grayish purple to brown; top convex to flat or slightly depressed; surface sticky when moist; flesh thick and soft. **Gills:** Pale gray to purplish brown. **Stalk:** White; prominent ring; smooth above ring and cotton-like scales below. **Veil:** White, membranous; forms a prominent ring on stem. **Size:** Cap to 6" (15 cm) across. Stalk to 6" (15 cm) long.

Season August to November.

Habitat On the ground, in coniferous forests or on well-decayed wood.

Range Northern hemisphere, Pacific Northwest and northern California.

Edibility Possibly poisonous.

Notes The lacerated stropharia is a handsome species that is often found at higher elevations. Sometimes it grows along with the questionable stropharia (see above).

Blue-green Stropharia *Stropharia aeruginosa*

Other Names Green stropharia, verdigris mushroom.
Description Solitary or in small groups. **Spore Print:**
Dark purplish brown. **Cap:** Blue-green fading to yellow,
white flecks often present from veil; bell-shaped or convex to flat; surface slimy when moist; margin often covered with veil remnants. **Gills:** Purplish brown; crowded
and broad; adnate (attached). **Stalk:** White to green or
blue; smooth above and scales below. **Veil:** White; cotton-like, evanescent (temporary) ring. **Size:** Cap to 3¼"
(8 cm) across. Stalk to 4" (10 cm) long.
Season August to October.
Habitat On woody debris, in various coniferous and
deciduous forests.
Range Widespread in North America.
Edibility Generally regarded as poisonous; however, it is
apparently consumed in Europe.
Notes Few species of mushrooms produce a green cap,
and as a result this colorful species is easily identified. It is generally regarded as not having a distinctive
smell, but one reference describes it as smelling of "fresh tomatoes."

 # Sulphur Tuft *Hypholoma fasciculare*

Other Names Clustered woodlover, bitter
naematoloma; also known as *Naematoloma
fasciculare*.
Description Tufted. **Spore Print:** Purple-
brown to purple-gray. **Cap:** Sulfur yellow
to greenish yellow. **Gills:** Sulfur yellow
to greenish yellow maturing to purple-
brown. **Stalk:** Yellowish to tawny; often
with brownish stains; thin, normally
curved; solid. Veil: Light yellow; thin.
Size: Cap to 3½" (9 cm) across. Stalk to
4¾" (12 cm) long.
Season May to June; August to November; throughout the winter in California.
Habitat On decaying stumps, buried wood
or roots.
Range Widespread in North America.
Edibility Poisonous. This species causes gastro-intestinal upset in North America, and
several deaths have been reported in Europe and Asia.
Notes This common species is abundant in the fall and winter but it is also occasionally
found in spring. It is handsome, with a beautiful smooth yellow cap that is aptly named
since it normally grows in a tufted situation.
Similar Species Smoky-gilled Woodlover *Hypholoma capnoides* (see p. 48)

Smoky-gilled Woodlover *Hypholoma capnoides*

Other Names Conifer tuft; *Naematoloma capnoides*.
Description Clustered or tufted. **Spore Print:** Grayish purple to purplish brown. **Cap:** Yellow to orange-brown; top convex to flat; surface smooth; flesh thin. **Gills:** Gray when young, changing to purplish brown when older; crowded. **Stalk:** Varies from yellow beneath the cap to brown at base; slender. **Veil:** Small patches often attached to cap margin. **Size:** Cap to 2¾" (7 cm) across. Stalk to 4" (10 cm) long.
Season August to December.
Habitat On decaying conifers, especially Douglas-fir.
Range Throughout North America.
Edibility Edible with a mild taste.
Caution: see Similar Species, below.
Notes This species is readily identi-
fied with its gray gills and long,
slender stems, which often appear
to be extended. The smoky-gilled

woodlover tends to fruit later in the season than sulphur tuft and often replaces it completely at season's end in some areas.
Similar Species Sulphur Tuft *Hypholoma fasciculare* (see p. 47), a bitter-tasting, poisonous species that grows in a similar habitat.

Bristly Pholiota *Pholiota squarrosoides*

Other Names Sharp-scaly pholiota, sharpscales.
Description Clustered. **Spore Print:** Brown. **Cap:** Yellowish brown with no green tint, whitish between the scales; top convex to flat; surface (at maturity) sticky when dry and gelatinous below the scales when moist; sharp upright dry scales. **Gills:** White to brown; no greenish tinge on gills; crowded and narrow; adnate (attached). **Stalk:** Buff; surface very scaly. **Partial Veil:** Off-white; often hangs from margin. **Size:** Cap to 4" (10 cm) across. Stalk to 6" (15 cm) long.

Season September to October.
Habitat On decaying hardwood.
Range Throughout North America.
Edibility Edible, but many people suffer from gastric upset or mild poisoning after consuming this species. Several similar-looking species are poisonous. Eating is not recommended.
Notes The bristly pholiota, which grows on fallen hardwoods, is reported to be the most common of several similar wood-loving *Pholiota* species. Note that the cap of this species is sticky when it is dry.
Similar Species Scaly Pholiota *Pholiota squarrosa*, very similar, displaying a greenish tint with no gelatinous layer on the cap.

Gypsy Mushroom *Rozites caperata*

Other Names Gypsy, granny's nightcap; formerly *Pholiota caperata*.

Description Solitary or in small groups. **Spore Print:** Rust brown. **Cap:** Ochre to golden brown; convex with flattened tip, expanding at maturity, wrinkled; surface dry, young caps covered with a frosty bloom; flesh firm and thick. **Gills:** Tan to brownish; crowded. **Stalk:** White to tan; firm, solid. **Veil:** White; membranous; covers the gills first then forms a ring midway. **Size:** Cap to 6" (15 cm) across. Stalk to 5⅓" (13 cm) long.

Season September to November.

Habitat On the ground, in coniferous and deciduous forests with a preference for mature conifers, especially hemlock.

Range Pacific Northwest to northern California.

Edibility Edible and choice, with caution. The stem is tough and often discarded. This is a very good species for drying. **Caution:** see Notes and Similar Species (below).

Notes The gypsy mushroom is a distinctive species that is often collected for the table. To ensure you have collected it and not another species, verify that your specimen has brown spores, a distinctive ring on the stem and a wrinkled cap. Several poisonous species look similar to the gypsy, so be sure you are aware of the identifying features of the similar species listed below. This is not a

species for new pickers to try. If you are in doubt, ask an expert.

Similar Species Agrocybes or Earthscales *Agrocybe* sp., also possesses brown spores and often a ring but grows on grass, wood chips or roadsides. The caps vary in shape from convex to flat or somewhat umbonate (knob-like).

Corts *Cortinarius* spp., in members of this group, the veil lacks a ring and young specimens have a web-like covering over the gills.

Galerinas *Galerina* spp., also posses brown spores and often a ring on a slender stalk.

Violet Cortinarius *Cortinarius violaceus*

Other Name Violet cort.
Description Solitary to a few. **Spore Print:** Rust brown.
Cap: Violet to almost black; top convex to flat or slightly depressed; surface dry, covered in hairs or scales.
Gills: Purple to rusty brown; adnate (attached); widely spaced. **Stalk:** Violet to brown; often with a thickened base; ring zone present; fibrous. **Veil:** Violet; cobweb-like cortina. **Size:** Cap to 6" (15 cm) across. Stalk to 4¾" (12 cm) long.
Season September to October.
Habitat On the ground, in old-growth coniferous forests, especially Douglas-fir.
Range Throughout much of North America.
Edibility Edible with quite pleasant flavor.
Notes Cortinarius is the largest genus of all mushrooms. The violet cortinarius is not as common as some species but is often found in localized populations. The rich, vibrant color of this handsome species is distinctive and readily aids in identification.

Lilac Conifer Cortinarius *Cortinarius traganus*

Other Name Pungent cortinarius.
Description Solitary to gregarious.
Spore Print: Rusty brown. **Cap:** Violet to lilac, silky; broadly convex to flat or slightly umbonate; surface smooth and dry or fibrillose; veil remnants often hang from margin. **Gills:** Cinnamon to rusty brown; well spaced. **Stalk:** Lilac to purplish; surface thickly covered with veil fibrils; enlarged base; flesh rusty brown. **Size:** Cap to 5⅓" (13 cm) across. Stalk to 5" (12 cm) long.
Season September to October.

Habitat On the ground, in coniferous forests.
Range Northern North America.
Edibility Unknown. Rated by some to be indigestible but another authority rates it as **poisonous**. Eating is not recommended.
Notes The lilac conifer cortinarius often emits a fruity smell that is comparable to overripe pears—a scent that has been described by some as penetrating.

Cinnamon Cortinarius *Cortinarius cinnamomeus*

Other Names Cinnamon webcap; also known as *Dermocybe cinnamomea*.
Description Scattered or in small groups. **Spore Print:** Rusty brown. **Cap:** Yellowish brown; conical to convex, maturing to flat or slightly umbonate; surface dry; with fibrous scales. **Gills:** Yellowish to tawny. **Stalk:** Yellowish brown; with tiny scales; slender. **Cortina:** Temporary fibrous veil. **Size:** Cap to 2⅓" (6 cm) across. Stalk to 4" (10 cm) long.
Season September to November.
Habitat On the ground, in coniferous forests.
Range Pacific Northwest.
Edibility Unknown; however, other similar-looking species are **deadly poisonous**.
Notes The cinnamon cortinarius is a striking species that is easily identified in the field. It is actually a complex of several species that must be studied in detail to be differentiated.

 # Red-gilled Cortinarius *Cortinarius semisanguineus*

Other Names Red-gilled cort, redgill webcap; also known as *Dermocybe semisanguinea*.
Description Scattered or in small groups. **Spore Print:** Rust brown. **Cap:** Yellow to olive-buff; bell-shaped or convex to flat or umbonate; margin often uplifted as it ages; surface dry. **Gills:** Red; crowded; adnate (attached). **Stalk:** Yellow; base often with pinkish down; slender. **Size:** Cap to 2⅓" (6 cm) across. Stalk to 4" (10 cm) long.
Season July to November.
Habitat On the ground, in coniferous and deciduous forests.
Range Widely distributed in North America, including Pacific Northwest, California.
Edibility Unknown. Eating is not recommended.
Notes "Striking" is the best word to describe this handsome species. The red-gilled cortinarius is as colorful as it is distinctive, unlike many of the species in this large group. In fact, many Cortinarius species are not easy to identify—even for many mycologists. This species sometimes smells like a radish, but that quality is not an invitation to eat it. Some members of the *Cortinarius* clan have killed people—in some cases weeks after the mushrooms were eaten.

White Fibrecap *Inocybe geophylla*

Other Names Little white inocybe, white fibre head.

Description Scattered or in small groups. **Spore Print:** Brown. **Cap:** White; top cone-like to flat or umbonate; surface dry. **Gills:** White maturing to brown. **Stalk:** White to brown; may be thicker at base. **Veil:** White; fibrillose or cobweb-like. **Size:** Cap to 1½" (4 cm) across. Stalk to 2⅓" (6 cm) long.

Season July to November.

Habitat On the ground, in various forests and occasionally on very rotten wood.

Range Widely distributed throughout North America.

Edibility Poisonous.

Notes The white fibrecap is an easy species to identify with its distinctive features. It is a poisonous species that contains muscarine, a poison that was first identified in fly amanita (see p. 36).

Poison Pie *Hebeloma crustuliniforme*

Description Solitary or in groups or rings. **Spore Print:** Rust brown. **Cap:** Buff to brown; top convex to flat or slightly umbonate; margin often uplifted as it ages; surface smooth, sticky or greasy when moist; flesh thick. **Gills:** Brown; crowded and narrow. **Stalk:** White to brown; covered with fine powder or flaky; enlarged at base. **Veil:** Absent. **Size:** Cap to 4⅓" (11 cm) across. Stalk to 5¼" (13 cm) long.

Season September to November; September to May in California.

Habitat On the ground, under trees and in open areas.

Range Widely distributed in North America.

Edibility Poisonous.

Notes This attractive species, commonly found in the West, has a distinctive radish-like smell. Its unique common name is derived from the color of its cap, which is not unlike that of a piecrust. Strangely enough, its scientific name *crustuliniforme* means cookie-shaped, an interesting name choice for a poisonous species of mushroom.

False Chanterelle *Hygrophoropsis aurantiaca*

Other Names Also known as *Cantharellus aurantiacus*, *Clitocybe aurantiaca*.
Description Solitary or in small groups. **Spore Print:** White or cream. **Cap:** Yellow-orange to orange-brown; convex to flat or slightly depressed; margin often inrolled; surface felt-like; flesh thin. **Gills:** Orange; crowded and narrow; decurrent (gills running down the stem). **Stalk:** Yellowish to orange-brown; surface dry; equal or thicker at base. **Size:** Cap to 5½" (14 cm) across. Stalk to 4" (10 cm) long.
Season August to November; overwinters in California.
Habitat On rotting coniferous wood, on the ground or buried.
Range Widespread in North America.
Edibility Not edible. Some authorities report it as mildly poisonous, and there are reports of hallucinations after eating it.
Notes The false chanterelle can be quickly identified by its overall orange color and presence of true gills. (Chanterelles have blunt, gill-like folds rather than blade-like gills.) These features help the mushroom picker to distinguish it from the Pacific golden chanterelle (see p. 73). As well, the Pacific golden chanterelle often emits a wonderful apricot-like smell, whereas false chanterelle does not. It has been said that this species will not sit still for taxonomists—a statement that fits many other fungi as well.

Slimy Gomphidius *Gomphidius glutinosus*

Other Names Glutinous gomphidius, slimecap, slimy spike.
Description Scattered to clustered. **Spore Print:** Smoky gray to black. **Cap:** Gray to reddish brown; peg-like maturing to convex or flat; surface smooth and slimy; flesh soft and thick. **Gills:** Gray; well-spaced; decurrent; somewhat waxy. **Stalk:** White, yellowish at base; narrower at base. **Partial Veil:** Colorless; slimy; leaves a slight ring. **Size:** Cap to 4" (10 cm) across. Stalk to 4" (10 cm) long.
Season June to November.

Habitat On the ground, under conifers, especially spruce.
Range Throughout northern North America; southern mountainous areas.
Edibility Edible, with a slimy texture. The outer slimy layer is often removed before cooking.
Notes This cosmopolitan species is the most common and widespread member of its genus in North America. The slimy gomphidius is often added to soups and stews.

● Rosy Gomphidius *Gomphidius subroseus*

Description Solitary or in small groups. **Spore Print:** Smoky to black. **Cap:** Pink to rosy red; peg-shaped to convex or flat; surface slimy or sticky when moist. **Gills:** White or gray maturing to black; well spaced; decurrent; soft and waxy. **Stalk:** White above veil, dirty white below with a yellow base; surface slimy. **Veil:** White, translucent. **Size:** Cap to 3" (7.5 cm) across. Stalk to 3" (7.5 cm) long.

Season June to October in the Rocky Mountains; September to December along the coast.

Habitat On the ground, under conifers, especially Douglas-fir.

Range Northern North America.

Edibility Edible, but lacking in flavor. Be sure to remove the gelatinous covering before eating.

Notes The rosy gomphidius is an easy species to identify in the field because of its overall pink to reddish coloration. Only 2 genera possess black spores and decurrent gills: *Gomphidius* and *Chroogomphus*. This basic information aids in the identification of the two groups (genera).

Similar Species Clustered Gomphidius *Gomphidius oregonensis*, known for its pinkish gray cap and habit of growing in clusters. It is an edible and choice species.

● Wooly Pine Spike *Chroogomphus tomentosus*

Other Names Orange woollycap; formerly *Gomphidius tomentosus*.

Description Solitary to gregarious. **Spore Print:** Gray to black. **Cap:** Dull orange; peg-shaped to flat or slightly umbonate; surface dry and wooly; flesh firm. **Gills:** Yellowish changing to purple or brown; decurrent, distant and thick. **Stalk:** Orange to ochre; somewhat fibrillose (covered with fibers). **Partial Veil:** Orange; fibrillose, leaves hairy ring on stalk. **Size:** Cap to 3½" (9 cm) across. Stalk to 7" (18 cm) long.

Season August to October.

Habitat On the ground, in coniferous forests, especially under Douglas-fir and hemlock.

Range Northern Rocky Mountains, Pacific Northwest and northern California.

Edibility Edible.

Notes The dry cap of this species is unusual in this family. This species was only recently found to be edible. Its peg shape and orange color aid in identification.

Western Painted Suillus *Suillus lakei*

Other Names Matte Jack, lake's bolete; also known as *Boletus lakei*, *Boletinus lakei*.
Description Scattered or in small groups. **Spore Print:** Brown. **Cap:** Yellow surface covered with reddish brown scales; top convex to flat or slightly depressed; dry or sticky when moist. **Pores:** Yellow to reddish brown upon aging. **Stalk:** Yellow above the ring and below with reddish brown streaks, glandular dots are absent. Young specimens often stain a very weak blue color at the base. **Veil:** Varies from white to the color of the cap. **Size:** Cap to 6" (15 cm) across. Stalk to 4¾" (12 cm) long.

Season July through October, November to January in California.
Habitat On the ground, often associated with Douglas-fir.
Range Pacific Northwest, Rocky Mountains, California.
Edibility Edible, but coarse and bland.
Notes The presence of a veil on this bolete sets it apart from most members of this genus. It is also one of the most common boletes that grows in Montana and Idaho.

Short-stemmed Slippery Jack *Suillus brevipes*

Other Name Short-stalked slippery Jack.
Description Solitary to clustered in dense masses. **Spore Print:** Brown to cinnamon. **Cap:** Dark brown to yellowish brown, convex to flat; slimy when moist, does not bleed when bruised. **Pores:** Pale to olive-yellow when mature; do not turn blue. **Stalk:** White maturing to pale yellow; often very short; glandular dots not present or hardly visible. **Veil:** Absent.
Size: Cap to 5⅓" (13 cm) across. Stalk to 2¾" (7 cm) long.
Season May and June; August through November.
Habitat On the ground, in coniferous forests, especially 2- and 3-needle pines.
Range Pacific Northwest, California, eastern North America.
Edibility Edible. Rated as good-tasting, but the slimy skin must be removed first.
Notes Although this common species is called the short-stemmed slippery Jack, it some-

times has a longer stem. It is a slippery-topped bolete that is easily identified because it has neither a veil nor glandular dots on the stem, which are present on most members of the genus *Suillus*. This species is likely the most common slippery Jack found in the West.

Blue-staining Slippery Jack *Suillus tomentosus*

Other Names Blue-staining suillus, wooly-capped bolete, wooly pine bolete, poor man's slippery Jack, tomentose suillus.

Description Solitary to clustered. **Spore Print:** Olive-brown to cinnamon brown. **Cap:** Yellow to yellowish brown; covered with small hairs maturing to brown fibrous scales; top convex to flat; sticky to slimy when wet; bruises blue. **Pores:** Dark brown maturing to yellow; stains blue where bruised. **Stalk:** Yellow to yellowish brown; stains blue where bruised; covered with tiny glandular dots. **Veil:** Absent. **Size:** Cap to 8" (20 cm) across. Stalk to 6" (15 cm) long.

Season August through January.

Habitat On the ground, in coniferous forests, especially near 2-needle pines.

Range Pacific Northwest, northern California, Rocky Mountains.

Edibility Edible, but not highly regarded.

Notes This bolete tends to bruise blue, often very slowly. It may stain your fingers brown if you handle it. The mycelia of this species form a symbiotic relationship with several species of 2-needle pines.

 # Peppery Bolete *Boletus piperatus*

Other Name Also known as *Chalciporus piperatus*.

Description Solitary or in groups. **Spore Print:** Brown to cinnamon. **Cap:** Yellowish brown to reddish brown; convex to flat; dry to slightly sticky. **Pores:** Yellowish brown to brick red. Does not turn blue when bruised. **Stalk:** Similar to cap color; with bright yellow flesh and mycelium at the base. **Veil:** Absent. **Size:** Cap to 3¼" (8 cm) across. Stalk to 4¾" (12 cm) long.

Season September to November.

Habitat On the ground, in coniferous forests.

Range Throughout North America.

Edibility Uncertain. Some individuals believe that this species would make an excellent seasoning after it is dried. Another authority states that the taste of pepper disappears once it is thoroughly cooked, and yet another states that it is poisonous until it is thoroughly cooked.

Notes This spicy species is commonly found in many areas, including the Rocky Mountains, the prairies and north to Alaska.

Zeller's Bolete *Boletus zelleri*

Description Solitary, clustered or in small groups. **Spore Print:** Olive brown. **Cap:** Black to various shades of brown, frosty bloom on young caps; top convex to flat; dry and often wrinkled. **Pores:** Yellow; often staining blue when bruised. **Stalk:** Yellow to tan, young with tiny red granules, maturing to dark red above or throughout; firm. **Veil:** Absent. **Size:** Cap to 6⅓" (16 cm) across. Stalk to 4¾" (12 cm) long.
Season September through April.
Habitat On the ground, in mixed woods, deciduous and coniferous forests especially Douglas-fir.
Range Pacific Northwest south to California and Mexico.
Edibility Edible, with mixed reviews; some sources rate it highly; others find it slimy and tasteless.
Notes The dramatic coloration of this striking bolete makes it one of the easier species to remember. It is one of the earliest boletes to appear in the fall and it stays with us throughout most of the fruiting season.

 # Admirable Bolete *Boletus mirabilis*

Other Name Also known as *Xerocomus mirabilis*.
Description Solitary or in small groups. **Spore Print:** Olive brown to greenish brown. **Cap:** Dark reddish brown to chocolate brown; top convex to flat; surface varies from moist to dry. **Pores:** Yellow to greenish yellow. **Stalk:** Dark brown to reddish brown; rough surface; usually thicker at base. **Veil:** Absent. **Size:** Cap to 8" (20 cm) across. Stalk to 8" (20 cm) long.
Season September through December.
Habitat On or near the decaying stumps, trunks and logs of coniferous trees, including western red cedar.
Range Pacific Northwest, northern California, eastern North America.
Edibility Edible and choice, with a distinct flavor of lemon.
Notes This beautiful and striking species is an unusual bolete in that it grows on wood, preferring rotting hemlock. Admirable bolete is often attacked by a powdery white mold, golden hypomyces *Hypomyces chrysospermus*, rendering it inedible.

King Bolete *Boletus edulis*

Other Names Edible bolete, cep, steinpilz porcini.

Description Solitary, scattered. **Spore Print:** Olive brown. **Cap:** Reddish brown to yellow-brown; top convex; dry or sticky when moist. **Pores:** White or pale to yellow or brownish with age. **Stalk:** White, often with brown higher up; often thicker at base when young. **Veil:** Absent. **Size:** Cap to 12" (30 cm) across. Stalk to 10" (25 cm) long.

Season June through October.

Habitat On the ground, especially in sandy areas; favors conifers but is also is found in deciduous forests.

Range Alaska to central California; worldwide.

Edibility Edible and choice, often with a nutty or meaty taste. This species should not be eaten raw. It can cause stomach distress when not cooked thoroughly.

Notes The king bolete is a prized treasure for mushroom fanciers. Its firm, nutty-flavored flesh is a real treat to dine on. This mushroom can grow to a huge size, though the larger ones are often riddled with larvae. To ensure that a questionable specimen is a king bolete, verify that the pores do not stain blue. This species is excellent in so many ways. It can be baked or sautéed in casseroles or omelets, or served steak-style. In some areas, fly amanita (see p. 36) is used as an indicator species to locate sites where king boletes are likely to be found.

This edible bolete was eaten by a Douglas squirrel (Tamiasciurus douglasii).

Aspen Bolete *Leccinum insigne*

Other Names Aspen scaber stalk, aspen rough stem.
Description Scattered or in groups. **Spore Print:** Yellowish brown to brown. **Cap:** Orange to reddish brown; convex to almost flat; smooth to pitted when old; surface dry to slightly sticky when moist. **Pores:** Off-white to olive-buff; does not stain blue when bruised. **Stalk:**

White when fresh; matures with many small brown scabers (granular projections); may stain or turn bluish at base of stalk. **Veil:** Absent. **Size:** Cap to 6²/₃" (17 cm) across. Stalk to 6" (15 cm) long.
Season June through September.
Habitat On the ground; associated with aspen forests.
Range Alaska, along the Rocky Mountains south to Sierra Nevada and east to eastern North America.
Edibility Edible and good (see notes below).
Notes Aspen bolete is part of a complex of several very similar species; all of which are said to be edible. In sensitive individuals, however, they have caused digestive upsets. Some of these species turn black when cooked.
Similar Species **Red Aspen Bolete** *Leccinum aurantiacum*, a larger, hardier species that grows under aspen and conifers; stains burgundy red first, then changes to bluish gray.

 # Orange Birch Bolete *Leccinum testaceoscabrum*

Other Name Also known as *Leccinum versipelle*.
Description Solitary or in small groups.
Spore Print: Brown. **Cap:** Orange to pinkish tan when old; convex to widely convex when mature; surface dry. **Pores:** White to brownish. **Stalk:** White with many black scabers.
Veil: Absent. **Size:** Cap to 4" (10 cm) across. Stalk to 4" (12 cm) long.
Season July through September.
Habitat On the ground, under birch trees.
Range Alaska and the Pacific Northwest to northeastern North America.
Edibility Edible, with caution. Several people have reported unpleasant reactions to this species. Caution is advised.
Notes Orange birch bolete is abundant in Alaska. Like other boletes, its flesh keeps well when it is dried, but it turns dark when cut or cooked. If you wish to try this species, cook it very well and taste only a small portion.

Black-footed Polypore *Polyporus badius*

Other Names Black-leg; also known as *Polyporus picipes*.
Description Solitary or in small groups. **Spore Print:** White. **Cap:** Reddish brown; convex to flat or umbonate (knob-like); surface dry; flesh tough and thin. **Pores:** White maturing to brownish. **Stalk:** Tan above, black below or black throughout. **Size:** Cap to 8" (20 cm) across. Stalk to 2⅓" (6 cm) long.

Season August to October; also overwinters.
Habitat On branches and logs of dead deciduous and occasionally coniferous trees.
Range Northern North America, Pacific Northwest, California.
Edibility Too tough to eat.
Notes This splendid polypore is often found growing on the narrow branch of a fallen tree or on a downed log that has been rotting for some time.
Similar Species Elegant Polypore *Polyporus varius*, also has a dark stem but displays a smaller cap with a lighter coloration.

Tiger's Eye *Coltricia perennis*

Other Name Funnel polypore.
Description Solitary or in small groups. **Spore Print:** Yellowish brown. **Cap:** Yellow to brown; circular with concentric bands of color; slightly depressed; surface velvet-like, changes with zone; flesh very tough. **Underside:** Brown; pores. **Stalk:** Dark brown; dense.
Size Cap to 4" (10 cm) across. Stalk to 1⅔" (3.5 cm) long.
Season August to November.
Habitat On the ground, near roads and open areas, under conifers.
Range Widely distributed in North America.

Edibility Not edible.
Notes Tiger's eye favors, but is not limited to, sandy areas. Its common name is a wonderful description of the cap's coloration—especially light brown specimens.

Artist's Conk *Ganoderma applanatum*

Other Name Artist's fungus.
Description Solitary or in small groups.
Spore Print: Brown. **Fruiting Body:** Gray
to brown; knob-like when very young, flat
and shelf-like at maturity; often covered
in a fine brown powder (spores); flesh very
firm, cork-like and hard. **Underside:** White,
turns brown instantly upon being scratched;
pores. **Stalk:** Normally absent. **Size:** To 30"
(75 cm) across and 2" (5 cm) thick.
Season Year-round.
Habitat On stumps, trunks and logs of
hardwood trees, occasionally on wounds of
living trees.
Range Throughout North America.
Edibility Far too tough to be edible.
Notes This common species gets its name from its easily marked underside. Its spore-
producing capabilities are truly astounding—it has been calculated that a single large
specimen of artist's conk can produce 30 billion spores a day during the summer months, for
a total of 4.5 trillion spores annually! This is the source of the brown dust-like coating that
often covers the surface of this conk.

Dye Polypore *Phaeolus schweinitzii*

Other Names Dyer's polypore, dyer's mazegill.
Description Solitary or in small groups. **Spore
Print:** White. **Fruiting Body:** Orange to yellowish
when young, rusty brown center at maturity; fan-
shaped or circular; surface covered in felt-like
matted hairs; flesh soft and sponge-like.
Underside: Yellow to greenish maturing to
brown; pores pallid, maturing to greenish yellow,
yellow to reddish brown upon aging. **Stalk:** Color
similar to cap; tapered. **Size:** Cap to 12" (30 cm)
across. Stalk to 2⅓" (6 cm) long when present.
Season June to November.
Habitat On dead wood and on the ground from
roots of nearby conifers.
Range Northern North America, Pacific Northwest, California.
Edibility Possibly poisonous.

Notes This striking species gets its common name
from colorful young specimens that have been
used to produce vibrantly colored dyes. It is not
well liked by foresters, however, as it causes a
tree-butt rot, a serious disease affecting a wide
range of conifers, especially old Douglas-fir trees.

Close-up of underside.

Sulphur Shelf *Laetiporus sulphureus*

Other Names Chicken of the woods, chicken mushroom; formerly *Polyporus sulphureus*; also known as *Grifola sulphurea*.

Description Annual; solitary to overlapping clusters. **Spore Print:** White. **Fruiting Body:** Reddish orange to salmon, fading to yellow with age; fan-shaped to semi-circular; surface smooth. **Underside:** Sulfur yellow; pores. **Stalk:** Normally absent, very short if present. **Size:** To 28" (70 cm) across and 1½" (4 cm) thick.

Season May to November.

Habitat On dead and living deciduous and coniferous trees.

Range Alaska to California.

Edibility Edible when young, but be sure to cook it thoroughly. Many mushroom enthusiasts collect only the outer margin of young specimens; others collect the entire fruiting body for consumption. A few cases of violent reactions have been reported from the Pacific region, so if you try this species, try only a tiny portion, as you should when eating any wild mushroom. There could be a toxic strain along the Pacific coast, and specimens growing on eucalyptus in California

can cause gastric upset. Allergic reactions have also been reported by people who ate older specimens, or who consumed sulphur shelf with alcohol.

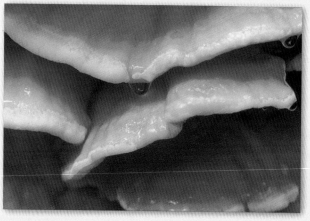

Notes Sulphur shelf is likely the only polypore that's considered edible. Fresh, young specimens often exude small orange or yellow droplets. This species grows quite large and may reach 50 lbs (22.5 kg) or more. Its texture is like that of chicken (not the taste, as some of its common names suggest).

Red-belted Polypore *Fomitopsis pinicola*

Other Name Red-belted conk.
Description Solitary or small groups. **Spore Print:** White to pale yellowish. **Fruiting Body:** White to light yellow when young, maturing to brown with a reddish concentric zone near margin; knob-like when young, shelf-like to hoof-shaped at maturity; flesh very hard and dense. **Underside:** White to yellowish; pores. **Stalk:** Absent. **Size:** To 30" (75 cm) across and 9" (22 cm) thick.

Season Year-round.
Habitat On stumps, trunks and logs of dead coniferous trees.
Range Northern North America, Alaska to California.
Edibility Too tough to be edible.

Notes The colors of this common polypore vary greatly. Research has shown that this species grows on more than 100 host tree species. The photographs included illustrate its many colorations. The red-belted polypore plays an important part in the ecosystem by recycling woody debris. Unfortunately, this can cause economic losses, as it hastens the decay of wood that could otherwise be harvested for lumber.

False Tinder Polypore *Phellinus igniarius*

Other Names False tinder conk, willow bracket, flecked-flesh polypore.
Description Solitary or in small groups. **Spore Print:** White. **Fruiting Body:** Brown maturing to grayish black; shelf-like; often with fine hairs or velvety when young; surface often cracked or furrowed; flesh very hard and woody. **Underside:** Brown to rusty brown. **Size:** Cap to 10" (25 cm) across.
Season Year-round.
Habitat On a wide variety of living deciduous trees.
Range Throughout North America.
Edibility Not edible.
Notes This bracket fungi is circumpolar. It is the agent that causes hardwood trunk rot in the trees that host it—not a major threat to the forest industry, but a local concern in certain areas for fruit trees, pulp-producing stands and recreation sites. False tinder polypore is known to live on many trees, including maple, alder, arbutus, birch, apple, dogwood, cottonwood and willow in the Northwest alone, and others elsewhere.

Tinder Polypore *Fomes fomentarius*

Other Names Tinder bracket, tinder conk, horse's hoof fungus, hoof fungus, amadou.
Description Solitary or in small groups. **Spore Print:** White. **Fruiting Body:** Gray to grayish brown; hoof-shaped, crustlike surface; flesh firm and cork-like. **Ventral Surface:** Gray to brown; pores. **Stalk:** Absent. **Size:** To 8" (20 cm) across and 1⅛" (3 cm) thick.
Season Year-round.
Habitat On dead stumps, trunks and logs of birch, alder, maple and other hardwood trees; occasionally on the wounds of living trees.
Range Northern North America.
Edibility Not edible.
Notes Tinder polypore is well known in Europe for its easy combustibility. It was also of great significance historically for 2,000 years, as the material for smoldering conks that were used in cauterizing wounds to stop bleeding. This fungus causes white spongy trunk rot in its host trees.

Rusty Gilled Polypore *Gloeophyllum saepiarium*

Other Names Yellow-red gill polypore; *Gloeophyllum sepiarium, Lenzites saepiaria.*
Description Solitary or in small groups. **Spore Print:** White. **Fruiting Body:** Dark brown, margin orange to yellowish or white when growing; shelf-like; surface smooth to hairy. **Underside:** Ochre to brown; gill-like pores; crowded and narrow. **Stalk:** Absent. **Size:** To 2¾" (7 cm) across and 4¾" (12 cm) long.
Season June to November, possibly overwinters.
Habitat On wood of conifers and occasionally hardwoods.
Range Throughout North America.
Edibility Not edible.
Notes The striking colors of the rusty gilled polypore are as beautiful as they are distinctive. This amazing species also fruits on docks and railway ties. The ventral surface is covered with gill-like structures that likely evolved from pores—or could pores have evolved from these type of structures?

Turkey Tail *Trametes versicolor*

Other Names Many-colored polypore, many-zoned polypore; also known as *Coriolus versicolor.*
Description Annual; clustered groups. **Spore Print:** White or yellowish. **Fruiting Body:** White, gray, brown, reddish brown and black, banded; rosette-like or overlapping; surface consists of alternating hairy and smooth bands; margin often wavy; surface dry; flesh very firm, thin and leather-like. **Underside:** White; pores. **Stalk:** Normally absent. **Size:** Cap to 4" (10 cm) across.
Season May to December, may revive during other season(s).
Habitat On stumps, trunks and logs of dead hardwood trees.
Range Throughout North America.
Edibility Not edible.
Notes The concentric patterns produced by this species are always a special treat to view. The colors are variable, but the pattern is quite consistent. Turkey tail is medicinally important in Japan, where it is known as kawaratake and sold as the extract Coriolus (its former genus). It is used as a cure for cancer, and research indicates that it may indeed have anti-cancer properties. **Similar Species Hairy Curtain Crust** *Stereum hirsutum*, closely resembles turkey tail but lacks tubes or pores. Its ventral surface is orange to buff, varying from smooth to somewhat bumpy.

Underside.

Conifer Coral Hericium *Hericium abietis*

Other Names Western coral hedgehog, coral hydnum, bear's head, goat's beard, pom pom du blanc.
Description Solitary or in small groups. **Spore Print:** White. **Fruiting Body:** Off-white to salmon-buff; mass of branches, spines clustered; flesh soft. **Spines:** Same as branches; may reach 1" (2.5 cm) but usually to ³⁄₈" (9 mm) long; tufts or clusters; soft and brittle. **Size:** To 30" (75 cm) across and high.
Season August to October.
Habitat On coniferous logs, especially Douglas-fir and fir.
Range Pacific Northwest, northern California.
Edibility Edible and choice.
Notes The conifer coral hericium is the most common species observed in the Pacific Northwest. This species often reaches a weight of 10 pounds (4.5 kg) and frequently reappears on the same log year after year. Imagine a record 100 lb (45 kg) specimen for the table—absolutely incredible for such a choice species!

Bearded Tooth *Hericium erinaceus*

Other Names Lion's mane hericium, old man's beard, pom pom du blanc, monkey head mushroom, unbranched hericium, satyr's beard, hedgehog mushroom; also known as *Hericium erinaceum*.
Description Solitary. **Spore Print:** White. **Fruiting Body:** White aging to yellow; upper portion solid and hairy. **Spines:** White; unbranched; large—to 3" (7.6 cm) long. **Stalk:** Absent. **Size:** To 16" (40 cm) across and 8" (20 cm) high.
Season August to November.
Habitat On living trees, especially oak and maple.
Range Pacific Northwest and California.
Edibility Edible while young but turning sour as it ages. Slow cooking is recommended.
Notes This distinctive fungus grows impressive spines that are long and unbranched. These characteristics separate it from its close relatives. The bearded tooth may also re-grow repeatedly, at the same spot on a tree, year after year. Not only is this species edible, but also it apparently has antibiotic properties! In laboratory studies, its chemical compounds have shown strong anti-microbial activity against a range of infectious agents. Research in this area continues.

Hedgehog Mushroom *Hydnum repandum*

Other Names Sweet tooth, pig's trotter, sheep's foot mushroom; *Dentinum repandum*.
Description Solitary to gregarious. **Spore Print:** White. **Cap:** Pale cream to reddish tan; top convex to flat or slightly depressed; surface smooth and dry; flesh firm and thick. **Spines:** White to pale orange; fragile. **Stalk:** White to pale orange. **Size:** Cap to 10" (25 cm) across. Stalk to 4" (10 cm) long.
Season July to November.
Habitat On the ground, in coniferous and deciduous forests.
Range Worldwide, throughout North America.
Edibility Edible and choice. Said by some to taste somewhat like oysters.
Notes The hedgehog mushroom is a wonderful species for beginners to collect for eating. It tastes great and does not have any similar-looking poisonous counterparts with teeth present. Young specimens taste much better than older, bitter-tasting individuals.
Similar Species Bellybutton Hedgehog *Hydnum umbilicatum*, a smaller species, typically with a belly-button-like depression in the center of the cap.

 # Hawk Wing *Sarcodon imbricatus*

Other Names Shingled hedgehog, scaly hedgehog, scaly tooth; also known as *Sarcodon imbricatum*, *Hydnum imbricatum*.
Description Solitary to gregarious. **Spore Print:** Brown. **Cap:** Buff to reddish brown; shingle-like, top convex to flat or slightly depressed; surface dry with upturned scales. **Spines:** Gray to brown; soft and brittle. **Stalk:** Brown; smooth. **Size:** Cap to 8" (20 cm) across. Stalk to 3¼" (8 cm) long.

Season June to October.
Habitat On the ground, under coniferous, deciduous and mixed-woods forests.
Range Throughout North America.
Edibility Edible, but nothing special and somewhat bitter.
Notes This common mushroom is often seen in late spring. Its common name comes from its close resemblance to the delicate layered feathers of the wing on a hawk. The smell of chocolate or smoke is often noted in descriptions of this mushroom.

Strawberries and Cream *Hydnellum peckii*

Other Names Bleeding hydnellum, red-juice tooth, Peck's hydnum.
Description Solitary to gregarious. **Spore Print:** Brown.
Cap: White to pink in young specimens or on the outer edge of older specimens, older specimens much darker in color; surface felt-like, clear red droplets often present on surface; top flat, maturing to widely convex. **Spines:** Pink to purplish brown, often with pale tips; short. **Stalk:** White to pink, felt-like, woody. **Size:** Cap to 6" (15 cm) across. Stalk to 3" (7.5 cm) long.
Season September to October.
Habitat On the ground, in coniferous forests.
Range Alaska to northern California and Rocky Mountains.
Edibility Inedible.
Notes As the many common names of this wonderful species suggest, it exudes droplets of "red juice" in wet weather. Young specimens have been described as resembling "Danish pastry topped with strawberry jam." Indeed, this striking mushroom is well named and one of the easiest species to identify. It and others in its genus are highly rated for their blue and green hues, which are used to dye yarn.

Ear Pick Fungus *Auriscalpium vulgare*

Other Names Pinecone tooth, earspoon fungus.
Description Solitary to a few. **Spore Print:** White. **Cap:** Light brown to black; kidney-shaped, top broadly convex to flat; flesh thin and tough. **Spines:** White to flesh-colored; short, fine and crowded. **Stalk:** Brown to black; attached to one side of the cap; with dense hairs. **Size:** Cap to 1½" (4 cm) across. Stalk to 4" (10 cm) long.
Season August to November.
Habitat On decaying, fallen conifer cones, including pines and Douglas-fir. It has also been noted to grow on spruce needles.
Range Throughout North America.
Edibility Unknown, but too small and tough to be edible.
Notes The ear pick fungus is another species with a very restricted habitat—various decaying coniferous cones or needles. It is not observed often, possibly because it is so small.

Strap Coral Fungus *Clavariadelphus ligula*

Other Names Strap coral, strap-shaped coral.
Description Scattered to gregarious. **Spore Print:** White to yellowish. **Fruiting Body:** Buff to reddish-brown; club-shaped, occasionally forked; surface smooth or with some wrinkling; white threads (mycelia) may be visible at base; flesh pithy. **Size:** To ⅝" (1.5 cm) across and 4" (10 cm) high.
Season July to November.
Habitat On the ground, under conifers.
Range Northern North America, California.
Edibility Not edible.
Notes Strap coral can produce tremendous fruitings in localized areas under conifers with rich soil. This species is sometimes favoured by slugs that nibble away at the tip of its fruiting body.
Similar Species **Pestle-shaped Coral Fungus** *Clavariadelphus pistillaris*, a larger species that is found growing under hardwoods.

 # White Spindles *Clavaria vermicularis*

Other Names Fairy fingers, white worm coral; also known as *Clavaria fragilis*.
Description Scattered, tufted or in small groups. **Spore Print:** White.
Fruiting Body: White; slender, spindle-shaped; surface dry; flesh brittle.
Stalk: Not separable from fruiting body.
Size: To ³⁄₁₆" (5 mm) across and 6" (15 cm) high.
Season July to September.
Habitat On the ground, in woods and open areas.
Range Widespread; including Pacific Northwest and California.
Edibility Edible.
Notes The fruiting bodies of white spindles resemble slender and rather irregular wax candles. As the various common names indicate, this species can resemble fingers, worms and various other objects. It requires moist conditions to produce its fruiting bodies, which often appear translucent.

Purple Fairy Club *Clavaria purpurea*

Other Name Purple club coral.
Description A few scattered to gregarious. **Spore Print:** White.
Fruiting Body: Purple; branches spindle-shaped, clustered; flesh fragile and brittle. **Stalk:** Absent.
Size: To 4¾" (12 cm) high.
Season July to October.
Habitat On wet ground, in coniferous forests.
Range Pacific Northwest and Rocky Mountains.
Edibility Edible, but not highly regarded.
Notes This handsome species is easily identified by its distinctive shape and color. Its branches suggest purple worms arising from the soil.

Crested Coral Fungus *Clavulina cristata*

Other Names Crested coral, wrinkled coral, white-crested coral fungus; formerly *Clavaria cristata*.
Description Solitary to gregarious. **Spore Print:** White. **Fruiting Body:** White when fresh; profusely branched tufts with tips that are fringed or crested; surface dry; flesh soft and fragile. **Stalk:** Short, or may be absent. **Size:** To 2" (5 cm) across and 4¾" (12 cm) high.
Season June to October.
Habitat On the ground, under conifers, especially western hemlock and Douglas-fir.
Range Throughout North America.
Edibility Edible, but opinions vary widely regarding taste. Be sure to not eat those specimens that have turned grayish to bluish (see below).

Notes Crested coral is found in the temperate regions of the northern hemisphere. It is often parasitized by another fungus, an ascomycete, *Helminthosphaeria clavariae*. When this species infects crested coral, it transforms it into a gray or bluish color. As a result, the mushroom becomes inedible and possibly poisonous.

Pink Coral Mushroom *Ramaria formosa* complex

Other Name Yellow-tipped coral.
Description Solitary or in small groups. **Spore Print:** Yellow. **Fruiting Body:** Pink; profusely branched; surface smooth; flesh brittle. **Stalk:** Pink, white at base; fleshy base.
Size: To 8" (20 cm) high and wide.
Season July to November.
Habitat On the ground, under coniferous and deciduous trees.
Range Throughout North America.
Edibility Poisonous. Some look-alike species are believed to have a laxative effect. Eating is not recommended.
Notes The striking pink coral mushroom complex is actually several similar species that are well known for being difficult to distinguish. More research is required.

 # Cauliflower Mushroom *Sparassis crispa*

Other Names Eastern cauliflower mushroom; also known as *Sparassis radicata*.
Description Solitary. **Spore Print:** White. **Fruiting Body:** White or cream maturing to buff; flattened leaf-like branches or lobes arranged in a large mass; surface smooth; flesh firm.
Size: To 12" (30 cm) across and 10" (25 cm) high.
Season July to October.
Habitat On the ground, in mature coniferous forests near stumps or at the base of trunks.
Range Widespread in North America.
Edibility Edible and choice. Cleaning this species is always difficult.
Notes The remarkable cauliflower mushroom is a parasite on the roots of pines and Douglas-firs. Individual specimens may reach 3 feet (91 cm) across and weigh up to 40 pounds (18 kg).

If you harvest this species, be sure to cut it off at ground level, leaving the base in the ground and removing only the upper "leafy" fruiting body. This will allow the species to fruit year after year at the same site.

Pig's Ear Gomphus *Gomphus clavatus*

Other Names Pig's ear, clustered chanterelle, violet chanterelle; *Cantharellus clavatus, Nevrophyllum clavatum*.
Description Scattered to clustered. **Spore Print:** Tan to ochre. **Cap:** Light purple to yellowish tan; top flat with a depressed center and wavy margins; surface varies from moist to dry; flesh firm and thick. **Ventral Side:** Purple to tan; prominent forked wrinkles or folds; firm and solid. **Stalk:** Purple to tan; continuous with cap; two or more often fused together. **Size:** To 6" (15 cm) across and 8" (20 cm) high.
Season August to October.
Habitat On the ground, under conifers, especially spruce and fir.
Range Northern North America, Pacific Northwest and northern California.
Edibility Edible and choice.
Notes Chanterelles do not produce true gills; instead they produce thick-edged wrinkles with veins that appear to be gills. The wrinkles in pig's ear gomphus are prominent, but not necessarily reminiscent of a pig's ear. A beautiful lavender dye made from this mushroom is used to dye wool. This species is more common at higher elevations of 2,000 ft (600 m) and higher.

Woolly Chanterelle *Gomphus floccosus*

Other Names Scaly vase chanterelle, scaly chanterelle; also known as *Cantharellus floccosus*.
Description Solitary to clusters. **Spore Print:** Ochre. **Cap:** Bright red to orange; trumpet-shaped top depressed maturing to a hollow center; surface covered with cotton-like or wool-like scales; flesh fibrous. **Ventral Side:** White to cream colored; deep, forked ridges. **Stalk:** White to orange; pronounced tapering; hollow at maturity. **Size:** To 6" (15 cm) across and 8" (20 cm) high.
Season June to October.
Habitat On the ground, in coniferous forests.
Range Pacific Northwest, California and the Rocky Mountains.
Edibility Eating is not recommended. Some reports say it is delicious; others say it causes gastric upset, nausea and diarrhea. This species has a sour taste and contains nor-caperoic acid, an indigestible acid that has been shown to enlarge rat livers.
Notes The woolly chanterelle is a colorful and distinctive species that is always a wonderful treat to observe.

Pacific Golden Chanterelle *Cantharellus formosus*

Other Name
Incorrectly known as *Cantharellus cibarius*.

Description
Solitary to scattered. **Spore Print:** Pink. **Cap:** Deep orange; top convex when young maturing to depressed or vase-shaped; margin inrolled, surface smooth. **Ventral side:** Pinkish maturing to orange; deeply decurrent (gills running down stem), forked with cross folds.

Stalk: Similar to underside, tapered downward. **Size:** Cap to 4¾" (12 cm) across. Stalk to 3½" (9 cm) long.

Season July to November.

Habitat On the ground, under conifers, especially western hemlock, Douglas-fir and spruce.

Range Pacific Northwest, California.

Edibility Edible and choice.

Notes The Pacific golden chanterelle produces a faint fruity aroma of apricots or peaches. It has been designated the official state mushroom of Oregon. This species is a favorite of mushroom gourmets throughout its range. It is prized for its great taste, and it is normally free of maggots. Large volumes of this species, as well as the golden chanterelle and white chanterelle (see Similar Species, below), are featured in restaurants in the area, as well as being shipped to chefs in Europe.

In the past, this species was identified as the golden chanterelle *Cantherellus cibarius*, but its identification was recently revised after genetic studies verified that the species found in the Northwest is a separate species, the Pacific golden chanterelle. The golden chanterelle is wide-ranging species with a pale yellow to cream-colored spore print. Its underside is normally a deeper yellow-orange than its Pacific counterpart.

Similar Species White Chanterelle *Cantharellus subalbidus*, another excellent-tasting species with an overall ivory coloration.

False Chanterelle *Hygrophoropsis aurantiaca*, an inedible species that is orange overall (see p. 53).

Jack O'Lantern Mushroom *Omphalotus olivascens*, a toxic look-alike that is often mis-identified as chanterelle. It has sharp-edged gills and normally grows in large clusters on buried roots and at the base of stumps. It commonly grows from Oregon to California.

Close-up of gill-like folds on the ventral side.

Funnel Chanterelle *Cantharellus infundibuliformis*

Other Names Winter chanterelle, yellow foot; considered by some to be the same as *Cantharellus tubaeformis*.
Description Scattered or in small groups. **Spore Print:** Cream to yellowish. **Cap:** Yellow to dark brown; top convex to flat and finally depressed into a funnel shape; surface smooth; flesh thin but rather tough. **Ventral Side:** Yellow to brown or violet; well-spaced folds. **Stalk:** Orange-yellow to yellowish; smooth; may be grooved or flattened; hollow at maturity. **Size:** Cap to 4⅓" (11 cm) across. Stalk to 3¼" (8 cm) long.
Season July to October; December to February in California.
Habitat On moss, humus or rotting wood in bogs and coniferous forests.
Range Northern North America.
Edibility Edible.
Notes The winter chanterelle favors cool temperatures, as its common name suggests. At times it can be very abundant. There are several closely related species in this group or complex of chanterelles.

 # Blue Chanterelle *Polyozellus multiplex*

Other Name Clustered blue chanterelle.
Description Clustered. **Spore Print:** White. **Cap:** Deep violet to bluish black; surface smooth; many fan-shaped lobes, margin wavy, lobed arrangement; flesh soft and brittle. **Ventral Side:** Purple with a bloom (powder-like covering); smooth, netted or with veins, occasionally pore-like. **Stalk:** Violet to bluish black; fused to base. **Size:** Cap to 4" (10 cm) across. Stalk to 2" (5 cm) long. Individuals often merge to form fused masses that can reach 39" (1 m) across.

Season June to October.
Habitat On the ground, under spruce and fir trees.
Range Northern North America; Pacific Northwest to northern California, Rocky Mountains.
Edibility Edible, but ratings vary greatly from delicious to inferior.
Notes The rich color of the blue chanterelle sets it apart from most mushrooms. It is uncommon in many areas, but in some old-growth forests it fruits regularly. Although this species closely resembles a chanterelle, the shape of its spores suggest it is likely a member of the genus *Thelephora*.

Toothed Jelly Fungus *Pseudohydnum gelatinosum*

Other Names Cat's tongue, jelly tooth, quivering spine fungus, white tooth jelly fungus;
also known as *Tremellodon gelatinosum*.
Description Solitary or in small groups. **Spore Print:** White. **Fruiting Body:** Off-white to
brown; fan-shaped or spoon-shaped; surface smooth; flesh rubber-like. **Underside:** Off-
white to brown; lined with teeth. **Stalk:** Similar to upper portion in color and texture; often

lateral from its wood substrate. **Size:** Cap
to 3" (7.5 cm) across. Stalk to 2⅓" (6 cm)
long.
Season September to November.
Habitat On stumps, trunks and logs in
coniferous forests.
Range Throughout North America.
Edibility Edible, but lacks flavor.
Notes The toothed jelly fungus is a
remarkable species that has evolved teeth,
unlike other members of its family. A hand
lens will reveal these rubber-like teeth, or
spines, which are similar to a cat's tongue.
This interesting species also occurs in
Australia and Europe.

 # Apricot Jelly Fungus *Tremiscus helvelloides*

Other Names Apricot jelly mushroom,
candied red jelly fungus; also known as
Phlogiotis helvelloides.
Description Solitary to gregarious. **Spore
Print:** White. **Fruiting Body:** Apricot
to pink; spatula-shaped or funnel-like;
surface smooth; flesh rubber-like. **Ventral
Surface:** Apricot to pink; surface smooth
or lightly veined. **Stalk:** Continuous with
cap. **Size:** To 4" (10 cm) across and 7"
(18 cm) high.
Season May to October.
Habitat On the ground, in coniferous
forests or on stumps, trunks and logs.
Range Widespread in North America, most
abundant in the Pacific Northwest.
Edibility Edible, but not tasty.
Notes This striking fungus is a treasure
to discover, but often difficult to see with
its apricot coloration. Young specimens
of apricot jelly fungus are often pickled
or candied; they are also a great, colorful
addition to salads—raw. They make even
better photographic subjects!

Brown Witch's Butter *Tremella foliacea*

Other Names Leafy brain, leafy jelly fungus, jelly leaf.
Description Solitary or in small groups. **Spore Print:** White to yellowish. **Fruiting Body:** Brown; leaf-like to flabby or gelatinous when moist. **Stalk:** Absent. **Size:** To 4" (10 cm) across and 8" (20 cm) high.
Season July to November.
Habitat On dead hardwood trunks and logs.
Range Throughout North America.
Edibility Edible, but not tasty.
Notes Brown witch's butter has been described as seaweed-like in appearance—a good comparison when it is fresh. This jelly is not as common as its colorful counterpart, witch's butter *Tremella mesenterica* (see p. 77).

Golden Jelly Cone *Guepiniopsis alpina*

Other Names Alpine jelly cone; also known as *Guepiniopsis alpinus*, *Heterotextus alpina*.
Description Scattered or in small groups.
Spore Print: Yellowish. **Fruiting Body:** Yellow to orange; cone-shaped, top slightly depressed; flesh gelatinous. **Stalk:** Present, but consists only a point where the fungus attaches to the substrate. **Size:** To 1" (2.5 cm) across and ½" (1 cm) high.
Season May to June, October to November.
Habitat On stumps, trunks and logs of coniferous trees.
Range Pacific Northwest and Rocky Mountains.
Edibility Unknown.
Notes The color of this jelly changes with its moisture content, varying from yellow when moist to orange when dry. This species appears in two separate well-defined fruiting seasons: usually just after the snow melts, and then again in the autumn.

Orange Jelly *Dacrymyces palmatus*

Description Scattered to gregarious. **Spore Print:** Yellowish. **Fruiting Body:** Orange; lobbed mass, white basal attachment; flesh gelatinous. **Stalk:** Absent. **Size:** To 2⅓" (6 cm) across and 1" (2.5 cm) high.
Season May to November.
Habitat On coniferous wood.
Range Throughout North America.
Edibility Edible but not tasty. It's great for adding color to green salads.

Notes This common species is often abundant in very moist areas. When moisture levels fall, the orange jelly shrivels and is restored to its original shape during the next rainfall.
Similar Species **Witch's Butter** *Tremella mesenterica*, normally a larger, yellowish species, with flattened lobes. It lacks the white basal attachment and grows on deciduous wood. A microscope can also help to identify this species—witches' butter does not have the tuning fork-shaped basidia (spore-producing cells) that are present in orange jelly.

 # Small Staghorn Jelly Fungus *Calocera cornea*

Other Name Clublike tuning fork.
Description Solitary to clustered. **Spore Print:** Yellowish. **Fruiting Body:** Dull yellow; club-like, gelatinous, unbranched or sparingly branched; surface slimy when moist. **Size:** To 4¾" (12 cm) high.
Season September to November.
Habitat On deciduous wood.
Range Widespread in North America.
Edibility Unknown.
Notes The small staghorn jelly fungus often grows from cracks in decaying logs. It is a tough species that shrivels into a hard, horny mass but revives when it rains.
Similar Species **Staghorn Jelly Fungus** *Calocera viscosa*, a larger and brighter yellow species that displays forked branches.

Western Giant Puffball *Calvatia booniana*

Other Name Boone's puffball.
Description Solitary or in small groups. **Fruiting Body:** White maturing to brown; surface warts maturing into shallow plates, dry; flesh white maturing to brown, firm maturing to powdery. **Stalk:** Absent. **Size:** Normally to 2' (60 cm) across and 1' (30 cm) high.
Season July to August.
Habitat On the ground, in arid areas including sagebrush country.
Range Alberta to New Mexico and California.
Edibility Edible and choice when the interior is not discolored. Unfortunately, it has been known to have a laxative effect on some individuals.
Notes It's not often that a single mushroom slice will fill a frying pan. Such is often the case with this fine, large, edible species, which can reach an impressive 50 lbs (22½ kg). Only eat those specimens that are prime, without any discoloration or, of course, maggots! This was one of the important edible species in pioneer days.
Similar Species **Giant Puffball** *Calvatia gigantea*, another large, somewhat uncommon species that grows along the coast. Its outer plates are larger and its shape is usually closer to round.

 Pear-shaped Puffball *Lycoperdon pyriforme*

Other Name Stump puffball.
Description Solitary to gregarious.
Spore Mass: White, later turning yellowish and eventually brown; firm maturing to powdery. **Fruiting Body:** White then yellowish and eventually brown; club-shaped to pear-shaped; surface smooth or with a few tiny spines; apical pore forms at top to release spores.
Size: To 1¾" (4.5 cm) across and 2" (5 cm) high.
Season July to November.
Habitat On decaying wood, stumps and similar materials.
Range Throughout much of North America.
Edibility Edible and choice when young. They quickly become bitter as they age.
Notes This wonderful species is easily identified and often collected in large numbers since it tends to be abundant. As with all puffballs, only those that are pure white inside, before they are past prime, should be collected. Try this puffball sliced, dipped in egg, coated with cracker crumbs and fried in a hot skillet.
Similar Species **Various Amanitas** *Amanita* spp., buttons may look like puffballs. To be sure, slice them in half to reveal the flesh inside. An amanita will show the parts of a mushroom rather than a solid spore mass.

Dusky Puffball *Lycoperdon nigrescens*

Other Names Black puffball, dark puffball; also known as *Lycoperdon foetidum*.

Description Solitary to small groups. **Fruiting Body:** Blackish brown, fading to yellow when aged; pear-shaped; surface dry, covered with short spines, which drop off and leave scars; flesh firm. **Stalk:** Absent. **Size:** To 2" (5 cm) across and 3¼" (8 cm) high.

Season August to October; August to April in California.

Habitat On the ground, in forests, especially conifers.

Range Wide ranging in North America; along Pacific coast.

Edibility Edible.

Notes The short spines of the dusky puffball are made up of compressed hairs. This handsome species is also found in Europe.

Gem-studded Puffball *Lycoperdon perlatum*

Other Names Gemmed puffball, common puffball, devil's snuffbox; formerly *Lycoperdon gemmatum*.

Description Solitary to gregarious. **Spore Mass:** White when fresh, later turning yellowish and eventually brown; firm maturing to powdery. **Fruiting Body:** White when fresh, later turning yellowish and eventually brown; round to pear-shaped; a single pore develops on top for release of spores at maturity; surface covered with white, gray or brown cone-shaped spines (which fall off as it matures). **Size:** To 3.5" (9 cm) across and 4" (10 cm) high.

Season July to October.

Habitat On the ground, along roads, in woods, in the open and other sites.

Range Throughout North America.

Edibility Edible and choice when young.

Notes The gem-studded puffball is believed to be the most common woodland puffball in North America. It is an easy species to identify and collect for the table. To ensure you have the correct species, slice the mushroom in half to reveal the white, undifferentiated flesh inside. If your specimen does not fit that description, discard it.

Meadow Puffball *Vascellum pretense*

Other Names Field puffball, western
lawn puffbowl; formerly *Lycoperdon
hiemale*; also known as *Vascellum
depressum*.
Description Solitary to gregarious. **Spore Mass:** White maturing
to brown. **Fruiting Body:** White to
brown; round to turban-shaped;
surface covered with minute spines
or granules; large pore forms at top
to eventually bring the fruiting body
into a bowl shape; sterile base is
present. **Size:** To 2" (5 cm) across and
2" (5 cm) high.
Season September to November.
Habitat On the ground, in meadows, pastures, lawns and similar areas.
Range Throughout much of North America, especially along the Pacific coast.
Edibility Edible.
Notes This puffball is not rated as highly as many other edible puffballs. As with all puffballs, slice this one in half prior to cooking to ensure that it is white and firm, without any
yellowish discoloring.

 # Rounded Earthstar *Geastrum saccatum*

Other Names Sessile earthstar, nested earthstar.
Description Solitary to small groups. **Spore Print:** Brown. **Fruiting Body:** White to brown;
sack-like, outer wall rubbery, splits into 4–8 rays at maturity. **Rays:** Buff to tan; star-like;
normally free from debris; fleshy. **Spore Case:** Gray to brown; paper-like, fibrillose. **Size:** To
4" (10 cm) across.
Season July to October.
Habitat On the ground, in leaf litter of mixed woods and coniferous forests.

Range Widely dis-
tributed in North
America.
Edibility Not ed-
ible.
Notes This wonder-
ful species is the
most common of
several similar
species that may
be found in the
Northwest. None of
them are consid-
ered edible.

ASCOMYCETES

Ascomycetes are the division of the fungi kingdom that produce their spores within microscopic cells called asci, located inside the fruiting body.

Orange Peel Fungus *Aleuria aurantia*

Black Morel *Morchella elata*

Description Scattered to clusters.
Cap: Yellowish brown to brown or black; conical or bell-shaped; margin attached to stalk; surface dry and wrinkled (deeply enough to be considered pitted) with branching folds. **Stalk:** White or cream-colored maturing to tan; hollow. **Size:** Stalk to 8" (20 cm) long. Cap to 4" (10 cm) across.
Season April to May; year-round in California.
Habitat On the ground, in forests, especially conifers and aspen, and in disturbed urban areas.
Range Throughout North America.
Edibility Edible and choice. It has been noted also that black morels can cause an upset stomach, especially if alcoholic beverages are consumed. Be sure to cook them well—black morels should not be eaten raw.

Notes Under favorable spring conditions, black morels reach high populations in areas that have been burned one or two years previously. This species is quite variable in its appearance and may be a complex of several similar species. In some areas, the this species grows to a size much larger than average.

Early Morel *Verpa bohemica*

Other Names Wrinkled thimble morel; also known as *Ptychoverpa bohemica*.
Description Scattered to gregarious. **Cap:** Yellow-brown to tan; conical or bell-shaped; hangs from apex of stem, surface dry and wrinkled with branching folds; flesh firm and thin. **Stalk:** White to cream-colored maturing to brown; smooth, often with irregular shape; hollow. **Size:** Stalk to 6" (15 cm) long. Cap to 2" (5 cm) across.
Season March to May.
Habitat On the ground, in deciduous forests, especially cottonwood, aspen and alder.
Range Throughout North America.
Edibility Edible, with caution. This species agrees with most people who eat it in moderation. However, some of those who have eaten large quantities or eaten it repeatedly for several days, have experienced a loss of coordination. The drying of this species may enhance its taste, and may reduce the negative responses of some people. Be sure to cook this fungus well before consuming it, as you would with any mushroom.
Notes This morel marks the beginning of spring, arriving earlier than the black morel (see above). It is often present in large numbers, and since few flowering plants normally grow that early in the year, it is easily observed. This species is not considered to be a true morel, since the cap hangs from the apex of the stem.

Hooded False Morel *Gyromitra infula*

Other Names Saddle-shaped false morel, elfin saddle.
Description Solitary to gregarious. **Cap:** Reddish brown to dark brown; saddle-shaped or wrinkled; surface smooth; flesh thin and brittle. **Underside:** Light brown. **Stalk:** White to buff; smooth; hollow. **Size:** Cap to 6" (15 cm) across. Stalk to 4¾" (12 cm) long.
Season November to April.
Habitat On rotting wood and on the ground, in coniferous and deciduous forests.
Range Throughout North America.
Edibility Deadly poisonous. This species contains the toxin MMH (monomethylhydrazine), which can cause acute poisoning and death. **Do not eat.**
Notes The toxic compound MMH, found in this and other *Gyromitra* species, is the same chemical that is used as rocket fuel for space travel. Not only is the hooded false morel poisonous if eaten, but it also releases toxic fumes into the air if it is cooked. **Do not eat.** It is better left for space travel.

Brown Elfin Saddle *Helvella elastica*

Other Names Elastic saddle, smooth-stalked saddle, flexible lorchel; also known as *Leptopodia elastica*.
Description Solitary to scattered. **Cap:** Brown to grayish tan; saddle-shaped; surface smooth; flesh thin and brittle. **Underside:** White to buff or tan. **Stalk:** White or yellowish; surface smooth; slender. **Size:** Cap to 2⅓" (6 cm) across. Stalk to 5½" (14 cm) long.
Season July to November.
Habitat On the ground, in coniferous and deciduous forests.
Range Throughout North America.
Edibility Unknown.
Notes This elfin is quite distinctive with its long, slender stalk or stem.
Similar Species Hairy Elfin Saddle *Helvella latispora*, features an inrolled capped margin and hairy undersurface. A microscope is necessary to differentiate this close relative from the brown elfin saddle.
Hooded False Morel *Gyromitra infula* (see above), has a noticeably thicker stem.

Fluted Black Elfin Saddle *Helvella lacunosa*

Other Names Black elfin saddle, fluted black helvella.

Description Solitary or in small groups. **Cap:** Gray to black; saddle-shaped or convoluted; surface smooth or wrinkled; flesh thin and brittle. **Underside:** Gray to black. **Stalk:** White to black; smooth, fluted and convoluted with elongated holes. **Size:** Cap to 4" (10 cm) across. Stalk to 6" (15 cm) long.

Season October and November.

Habitat On the ground in grassy areas and coniferous or deciduous forests. It is also reportedly found on decaying wood.

Range Pacific Northwest and California.

Edibility Edible when cooked (see below). Correct identification is important, since the similar-looking hooded false morel (see p. 83) is toxic. **Caution is advised.**

Notes This species is edible if dried or parboiled for 3 to 5 minutes. It may contain a small amount of a toxic substance, monomethylhydrazine, which is released into the air when dried or removed by cooking.

This fluted black elfin saddle has been parasitized by a parasitic mold (Hypomyces cervinigenus).

Orange Peel Fungus *Aleuria aurantia*

Other Name Orange fairy cup.
Description Solitary or in small groups. **Cap:**
Bright orange; cup-shaped to saucer-shaped, flat
to wavy; margin often uplifted as it ages; surface
smooth and dry; flesh thin and fragile. **Underside:**
Light orange. **Stalk:** Absent or poorly developed.
Size: To 4" (10 cm) across.
Season May to October.
Habitat On the ground, in sand or soil along path-
ways, roads and grassy areas.
Range Throughout North America.
Edibility Edible, but not regarded as tasty, but it
does add color to salads.
Notes This species is aptly named with its thin
flesh, bright orange color and characteristic clusters. It is often served raw or in salads, to which
it adds color. The orange hue is caused by the
presence of carotene, which can be a good source
of vitamin A.

Green Cup *Chlorociboria aeruginascens*

Other Names Green stain,
blue stain.
Description Gregarious.
Fruiting Body: Blue-green,
sometimes with yellow; cup-
shaped to disk-like; margin
often slightly uplifted;
surface smooth or wrinkled.
Stalk: Blue-green; short.
Size: Cap to ³/₈" (1 cm)
across.
Season June to November.
Habitat On decaying deciduous logs.
Range Throughout North
America.
Edibility Hardly worth the
time.
Notes This species is often
noticed when a log is over-
turned and the distinctive
blue-green fungal threads are exposed. The pigment within this species turns the wood
greenish or bluish.

Purple Jelly-drop Cups *Ascocoryne sarcoides*

Other Names Brain jelly-drop cup, purple jellydisc; also known as *Coryne sarcoides*.
Description Scattered or in small groups. **Fruiting Body:** Flesh-colored to dark purple; lobed; gelatinous. **Stalk:** When present, short and colored like fruiting body. **Size:** To 3/8" (1 cm) across.
Season September to November.
Habitat On dead hardwood.
Range Throughout North America.
Edibility Unknown, but hardly worth the effort.
Notes In moist conditions, the lobes of this unique species swell into a gelatinous mass. Although purple jelly-drop cups resemble a jelly fungus (with spore-bearing basidia), they actually bear spore sacs called asci.

Jellied Birds Nest Fungi *Nidula candida*

Other Names Common gel bird's nest, gel birds nest.
Description In groups. **Taste:** White exterior, white to brown interior; deep mug-like shape, smooth inner wall; lid covers structure when young. **Eggs:** Gray to light brown; several disk-shaped without cords; embedded in gel. **Size:** To 5/16" (8 mm) across and 3/4" (2 cm) high.
Season Year-round.
Habitat On rotting wood, including branches and bark.
Range Throughout much of North America.
Edibility Not large enough to be of nutritional value.
Notes The "eggs" of bird's nest fungi are called peridioles (disk-shaped spore cases). They

are specially designed for dispersal in the rain by a technique referred to as splash-cup dispersal. When a raindrop hits the nest in just the right way, it projects the peridioles to an amazing 7' (2 m) away, dispersing spores to new areas. This is one of the most common species of several bird's nest fungi that occur in the Northwest.

Yellow Fairy Fan *Spathularia flavida*

Other Name Yellow earth tongue.
Description In small groups. **Fruiting Body:** Yellow; shaped like a canoe paddle; surface varies from smooth to wrinkled. **Stalk:** Yellow to ochre; slightly wider than fruiting body; hollow. **Size:** To 1¼" (3 cm) across and 4" (10 cm) tall.
Season August to November.
Habitat On rotting wood or humus.
Range Pacific Northwest, northern California.
Edibility Edible but small and reported to be tough.
Notes The scientific name *Spathularia* refers to the spatula shape of this unique group of fungi. Despite this species' bright yellow color, it is easily missed because of its small size. Therefore, it is likely more common than it seems.

Lobster Mushroom *Hypomyces lactifluorum*

Description Solitary to gregarious. **Fruiting Body:** Bright orange to red; completely engulfing its host mushroom; surface covered with minute pimples; flesh very firm. **Size:** To 12" (30 cm) across and 10" (25 cm) high.
Season July to October.
Habitat On the ground, in coniferous and deciduous forests.
Range Throughout North America; especially common in the West.
Edibility Edible and choice. This species is featured on the menus of many restaurants and is sold in Mexican markets.
Notes The lobster mushroom is a parasitic mold that attacks various species of *Russula* and *Lactarius*. The host species appears to include only white species such as the short-stemmed russula (see p. 15). No poisonings by this striking species have ever been reported. It is possible that the lobster mushroom could infect a poisonous host and become poisonous itself. To be sure, identify the host species as non-poisonous to ensure the lobster mushroom's edibility.

Bibliography

Arora, D. 1986. *Mushrooms Demystified*. Ten Speed Press, Berkeley CA.

Arora, D. 1991. *All That the Rain Promises, and More*. Ten Speed Press, Berkeley CA.

Bandoni, R.J., and A.F. Szczawinski. 1976. *Guide to Common Mushrooms of British Columbia*. B.C. Provincial Museum Handbook 24, Victoria BC.

Bessette, Alan E., et al. 2000. *North American Boletes: A Color Guide to the Fleshy Pored Mushrooms*. Syracuse University Press. Syracuse NY.

Bossenmaier, Eugene F. 1997. *Mushrooms of the Boreal Forest*. University of Saskatchewan Press, Saskatoon SK.

Fischer, David W., and Alan E. Bessette. 1992. *Edible Wild Mushrooms of North America: A Field-to-Kitchen Guide*. University of Texas Press, Austin TX.

Hall, Ian R., et al. 2003. *Edible and Poisonous Mushrooms of the World*. Timber Press, Portland OR.

Laessoe, T., A. Del Conte and G. Lincoff. 1996. *The Mushroom Book: How to Identify, Gather, and Cook Wild Mushrooms and Other Fungi*. DK Publishing, Inc., New York.

Lincoff, G.H. 1981. *The Audubon Society Field Guide to North American Mushrooms*. Alfred A. Knopf, New York.

McKenny, M., D.E. Stuntz and J.F. Ammirati. 1987. *The New Savory Wild Mushroom*. University of Washington Press. Seattle WA.

McKnight, Kent H., and Verna B. McKnight. 1987. *A Field Guide to Mushrooms: North America*. Peterson Field Guide Series. Houghton Mifflin Co., Boston, New York.

Miller, O.K. 1979. *Mushrooms of North America*. E. P. Dutton, New York.

Phillips, Roger. 2005. *Mushrooms and Other Fungi of North America*. Firefly Books, Buffalo NY.

Schalkwijk-Barendsen, Helene M.E. 1991. *Mushrooms of Western Canada*. Lone Pine Publishing, Edmonton AB.

Tylutki, E.E. 1979. *Mushrooms of Idaho and the Pacific Northwest: Discomycetes*. University Press of Idaho, Moscow ID.

Tylutki, E.E. 1987. *Mushrooms of Idaho and the Pacific Northwest, Vol. 2: Non-gilled Hymenomycetes*. University Press of Idaho, Moscow ID.

Acknowledgments

I would like to thank several people who assisted with this project.

Mary Schendlinger for her careful and patient editing.

Terry Taylor for his thorough and insightful scientific editing.

Jim Salt, who generously aided me in locating several mushroom species for photography.

Fidel Fogarty, Sharmin Gamiet, Paul Kroeger, David Tamblin, Terry Taylor and various members of the Vancouver Mycological Society, who were kind enough to identify and confirm the identification of several species of fungus and their photographs. Their knowledge and expertise is greatly appreciated.

Glossary

adnate: grown together, attached to.

adnexed: unattached, having a free edge, flag-like; opposite of adnate.

annulus: ring or annular ring.

asci: sac-like mother cells (of Ascomycetes) that contain spores.

basidia: mother cells (of Basidiomycetes) on which spores are produced.

canescence: dense covering of very fine, short white or gray hair.

cespitose clusters: many mushrooms emanating from a single point.

complex: group of very closely related, similar species represented by a particular species (e.g., *Armillaria mellea*).

cortina: veil with a cobweb-like or silky texture.

decurrent gills: gills that run down the stem (e.g., *Gomphidous* sp.).

distant gills: gills that are widely spaced.

fibrous: does not fracture like a piece of chalk.

free gills: gills that are not attached to the stem.

hyphae: mass of thread-like filaments that combine to make up the fungal mycelium.

mycelium: basic component of fungi, above and below ground; consisting of many hyphae.

partial veil: protective covering on some species of young mushrooms that extends from cap margin to stalk (e.g., *Stropharia* sp.).

pellicle: skin-like covering that is easily removed.

pileus: cap of a mushroom.

rhizomorphs: shoelace-like hyphae.

stipe: stem or stalk.

striate: finely grooved, covered with lines.

umbonate: having a bump in the center or a knob-like top.

universal veil: protective covering that covers the entire mushroom (or most of it) in its early stages (e.g., *Amanita* sp.).

veil: protective covering over some mushrooms; see partial veil and universal veil.

volva: sac or cup-like structure at stem base; lower remnants of universal veil.

Index

About the Author

Duane Sept is a biologist, freelance writer and professional photographer. His biological work has included research on various wildlife species and service as a park naturalist. His award-winning photographs have been published internationally, in displays and in books, magazines and other publications, for clients that include BBC Wildlife, Parks Canada, Nature Canada, National Wildlife Federation and World Wildlife Fund.

Today Duane brings a wealth of information to the public as an author, in much the same way he has inspired thousands of visitors to Canada's parks. His published books include *The Beachcomber's Guide to Seashore Life in the Pacific Northwest* (Harbour Publishing), *Common Birds of British Columbia* (Calypso Publishing) and *Wild Berries of the Northwest: Alaska, Western Canada and the Northwestern United States* (Calypso Publishing).

More Great Nature Books from
Calypso Publishing

Common Birds of British Columbia
J. Duane Sept

This full-color photographic guide features 136 species of birds found in British Columbia. Discover interesting facts about each species as well as descriptions, habitat and range. Handy tips are also included on how to bring birds closer, outfit yourself with birding equipment and attract birds to your backyard.

5.5" x 8.5" • 96 pages • 158 color photos • Softcover • $12.95 • ISBN 0-9730390-2-7

●●●●●●●●●●●●●●●●●●●●●●●●●●●

Wild Berries of the Northwest:
Alaska, Western Canada and the Northwestern United States
J. Duane Sept

Fruits and berries are all around us. Identify these fruits and their flowers on your next trip to the ocean, lake or woods with this full-color guide. Learn which species are edible and which are poisonous. An entire chapter of mouth-watering recipes is also featured. Enjoy!

5.5" x 8.5" • 96 pages • 169 color photos • Softcover • $12.95 • ISBN 0-9730390-8-6

●●●●●●●●●●●●●●●●●●●●●●●●●●●

Common Wildflowers of British Columbia
J. Duane Sept

This easy-to-use, beautifully illustrated guide helps you identify 142 species of wildflowers that grow in British Columbia. Lavish full-color photos and clear, understandable descriptions illuminate each of the common and uncommon flowers. Also included are little-known facts, edible species, notes on aboriginal use and a checklist.

5.5" x 8.5" • 96 pages • 145 color photos • Softcover • $12.95 • ISBN 0-9730390-9-4

These titles are available at your local bookstore or

Calypso Publishing
www.calypso-publishing.com